PLANT-B

COOKBOOK

101 DELICIOUS DIET RECIPES WITHOUT MEAT FOR COOK EVERY DAY INEXPENSIVE AND FLEXIBLE HEALTHY MEALS.

BOOST YOUR WEIGHT LOSS WITH A

30-DAY MEAL PLAN SPECIAL FOR BUSY PEOPLE

WILLY STONE

Table of Contents

Additionally, the information in the following pages is intended only for informational purposes and should thus be thought of as universal. As befitting its nature, it is presented without assurance regarding its prolonged validity or interim quality. Trademarks that are mentioned are done without written consent and can in no way be considered an endorsement from the trademark holder.

ALL ABOUT PLANT-BASED DIET

A plant-based diet is a diet that focuses on foods derived from plant-based sources. This includes vegetables, fruit, grains, legumes, meat substitutes, pulses, and nuts.

People have different interpretations of what a plant-based diet really is. Some people include little amounts of animal products such as fish and meat, while still focusing mainly on vegetarian foods. Diets that still include fish but cut out meat are called ***pescatarian*** *diets*. People who do not eat fish or meat but still include eggs and dairy are called ***vegetarians***, while ***Vegans*** cut out honey, gelatin, eggs, and all animal-derived products.

People that follow plant-based diets and consume a wide variety of vegetables, pulses, and fruits are likely to easier meet their *five-a-day target*. This is because they enjoy the vitamins, minerals, and *fiber* present in fruits and vegetables, which are all especially important for good health.

However, it is important to note that 'plant-based' does not automatically translate to 'healthy', especially when it comes to packaged and processed foods. Products such as certain vegetable fats, white flour, and refined sugar can technically be labeled as 'plant-based' since they really are plant-based, however, these foods should not make up the bulk of any plant-based diet if you desire to eat healthily.

The term plant-based was first coined in 1980 by biochemist Thomas Colin Campbell. He employed it when presenting his research on non-animal-product diets in a way he felt would not be clouded by politics.

Difference between A Vegetarian diet and A Plant-Based Diet

Most people assume that following a plant-based diet automatically makes you a vegetarian. This is not true.

Let's discuss the difference:

What is a vegetarian diet?

A vegetarian in the simplest of terms is a person that does not eat any poultry, fish, or meat. People choose to become vegetarians for several reasons – cultural, ethical, or religious reasons. A person might harbor concerns over the welfare of the animal or feel that the killing of animals for food is unnecessary. Another person might do so because they were raised in a religion or culture that considers animals as holy or sacred.

There exist different types of vegetarian diets. Most combine animal products – milk, eggs, honey – with plant-based diets. Others forbid all foods with animal products – milk, eggs, and honey. While some types of vegetarian diets allow the eating of fish, others do not.

A vegetarian diet can be healthy; however, it is worth noting that vegetarian diets allow the eating of refined and processed foods, salty snack foods, and even fast foods. This allows foods made with refined sugar or white flour, including bread, white rice, snack foods like potato chips and cookies, and sugary beverages. In essence, although a vegetarian diet can be healthy, the goal is not necessarily health-based but rather is eating meat-less foods with no animal products.

You are not eating healthy if you exclude meat from your diet but live on canned vegetables, refined grains, canned soups, salty snacks, and fruit juices, even though you are not eating any meat.

Does this make a vegetarian diet unhealthy? Not at all. A vegetarian diet is as healthy as you make it. You can decide to plan your meals carefully, taking care to exclude all unhealthy meals and ensuring you are getting enough of the important nutrients.

What is a plant-based diet?

In a plant-based diet, a person eats mainly fresh fruits, whole grains, legumes (peas, beans, etc.), unsalted nuts, vegetables, and healthy oils (olive oil, etc.).

You also avoid processed foods (most canned soups and foods), refined grains, snack-foods (cookies, potato chips), and sugar-sweetened beverages. Although poultry, meat, fish, and other animal products are allowed, they are restricted to little portions and are eaten less often. Most people who choose to follow a plant-based diet do so mainly for health reasons rather than other reasons – ethical, religious, or cultural. The health benefits of plant-based diets are numerous, especially for heart health.

WHY PLANT-BASED DIET

FOR YOUR HEALTH

Focusing on whole, plant-based foods is not just good for your waistline. Plant-based foods are good for your whole body, literally from your head to your toes. Studies have shown that people that follow a plant-based diet have a lower risk of high blood pressure and type 2 diabetes. They typically have an easier time getting the recommended servings of fruits and vegetables because their meals can be centered on plants. Even if you are not ready to give up meat entirely, your body can still benefit simply by replacing some of the meat you eat with plant-based foods.

People who eat a plant-based diet also tend to have a lower BMI (body mass index, a measure of body fat based on height and weight) and lower rates of obesity. This could be attributed to several things, but one simple reason is that fruits and vegetables are not very calorie dense. If you have ever struggled with portion control, vegetables are an easy way to fill up. Of course, simply eating a vegetarian diet is not necessarily a cure-all, and there are plenty of not-so-healthy vegetarian foods, but as you learn to incorporate healthy, plant-based foods into your diet, your body will reap the benefits.

FOR YOUR WALLET

There is a misconception that healthy eating has to be expensive, but it can actually be a cost-effective way to eat. A plant-based diet is quite a bit cheaper than a diet that includes animal protein. Plant-based proteins, like lentils and beans, are inexpensive protein sources, so cutting back on meat can significantly lower your grocery bill. For example, ground beef, relatively inexpensive meat, is typically between $3 and $4 a pound. If you were to purchase organic, grass-fed ground beef, it might be closer to $6 to $7 a pound. In contrast, a pound of lentils costs less than $2, and that would be enough lentils to feed a family of four! While fresh produce can occasionally be pricey, there are delicious frozen produce options that can be just as tasty, for a fraction of the cost.

FOR THE ENVIRONMENT

Eating a plant-based diet also has a positive effect on the environment. Producing 1 pound of animal protein uses 12 times more land, 13 times more fossil fuel, and 15 times more water than producing 1 pound of plant-based protein. In fact, a 2006 report from the United Nations found that raising animals for food generates more greenhouse gases than all the cars and trucks in the world combined. Whether it's for your own health or the health of the planet, eating less meat can have a positive effect on your life.

BENEFITS OF PLANT-BASED DIET

There have been numerous studies that have proved the power of a plant-based diet. Not just on your immediate health, but long-term health and in the prevention of chronic disease. However, as these research get more and more in-depth, it's been discovered that eating a plant-based diet goes beyond your physical health and well-being. Eating a plant-based also is beneficial for the environment, animal welfare, water scarcity, world hunger, and more! The benefits of going on a plant-based diet are numerous and are listed below, check them out and go plant-powered by starting a diet this week. Remember, when you fill your plate with the good plant stuff, there exists less room for acidic animal foods that will leave you tired and sluggish.

Improve Your Digestion

A lot has been said about gut health recently. There exist some foods for gut health and amazing gut-friendly recipes, however, the summary of it all plants. Plants are naturally full of fiber and fiber is the key to good digestion. Fiber adds bulk to your stool, while also regulating things and helping everything eliminate smoothly.

Reduce Your Risk of Chronic Disease

It isn't that a plant-based diet necessarily reverse disease, it is that research has proved that the Standard American Meat Diet promotes disease. People who are on diets full of processed foods, meat and dairy are at an increased risk for chronic diseases like cancer, diabetes, and heart disease.

Plant-based diets have been shown to have the opposite effect. People who eat a plant-based diet have reportedly low cases of some of the common chronic diseases - diabetes, some types of cancer, heart disease, Alzheimer's, etc. So, if the chronic disease runs in your family or you are just concerned about them, it is definitely a good and living saving idea to switch to a plant-based diet!

Naturally Boost Your Energy

Plants have really high in minerals and vitamins which are amazing for energy! They are rich in phytonutrients, antioxidants, and most times proteins and healthy fats, all of which are really great for your mood and brain. Plants are also easier to digest, thus provides our bodies with fast extra energy to expend. Plant-based foods are amazing for athletes and performance, which is why the number of professional athletes adopting plant-based diets keeps rising daily.

Get Healthy Hair, Skin & Nails

Our bodies are a reflection of what we put into them and because plants are so full of minerals and vitamins, they are particularly amazing for your hair and skin. Dairy, meat, and processed foods have all been shown to cause inflammation in our body, and most times, these inflammation are reflected on our skin. There is no guarantee that your skin would miraculously clear up the minute you start your plant-based diet, it would take some time. Be patient.

Lose Weight Effortlessly

Ever wonder why people recommend that you eat vegetables, fruits, and whole grains to lose weight although it's been proved that they are more nutrient-dense than processed foods? Plant-based foods have a lower calorie to volume ratio. Simply put, if you eat the same volume of food (say one pound) and then compare how much space it takes up in your stomach, plants will take up significantly less room. This means you will fill up more quickly eating plant-based diets while consuming fewer calories.

Lower Blood Pressure

A lot of the people living a plant-based diet have reported lower blood pressure. This is due to a high intake of potassium-rich diets. Potassium lowers blood pressure levels that would otherwise lead to anxiety and stress. Almost all seeds, vegetables, whole grains, legumes, fruits, and nuts contain a high quantity of Vitamin B6 and potassium helps lower blood pressure). Meat and most animal foods contain little potassium and most actually raise blood pressure and cholesterol.

Lowers Cholesterol

Talking about cholesterol, one of the major benefits you will receive from embracing a plant-based diet is lowered cholesterols. Most people do not know that plants do NOT contain cholesterol, even the saturated sources like cacao and coconut.

Better Blood Sugar

Eating fiber is the number one way to fight high blood. It has been proven to slow down the body's absorption of sugars in its bloodstream thus regulating your hunger level, additionally; it balances your cortisol levels that cause stress. Meat and other animal-based foods have been shown to raise blood sugar.

Lower Rates of Cancer

A whole-food plant-based, low-fat diet is the best way to improve your chances of avoiding cancer (while staying away from smoking and alcohol). Animal foods have been linked to an increased chance of cancer, especially breast and colon cancer.

Support the Environment & Our Planet

Eating a plant-based diet is one of the best things anybody can do for planet Earth. Animal agriculture causes more greenhouse gas emissions than the transportation sector in its entirety. It is also responsible for about 90% of the Amazon's deforestation as well as it being a big drain on our water supplies. Eating a plant-based diet, every day saves one animal, 10 pounds of CO2 emissions, and 1,100 gallons of water, and 30 square feet of forest. In a single day!!

Save Animals

And of course, the animals.

Make sure your plant-based meals are healthy

A plant-based diet can be healthy or not depending on your ability to avoid major diet pitfalls, like fat and sugar.
Use healthy cooking methods knowing just how to make get the most out of your vegetables.
Don't deep-fry your vegetables. Avoid highly processed foods like cookies and crackers.
Pick whole grains and ensure you limit sugary desserts. Go for 100% whole wheat bread and pasta and eat brown rice.

SHOPPING LIST AND SIMPLE MENU

MUST HAVE KITCHEN EQUIPMENT

Learning to eat in a new way of figuring out new methods for preparing food can feel challenging at first, but with the right tools in the kitchen, making these recipes will be a breeze. There are a few must-haves that I can't recommend enough. I also share some of my favorite nice-to-have kitchen equipment.

MUST-HAVES

Many of these must-have items are probably already in your kitchen. If not, consider investing in these tools, because you'll need them for the recipes in this book.

Sharp knife: Having a sharp knife is essential when preparing fruits and vegetables.

Knife sharpener: Even the sharpest knife gets dull after a while. You can find a small manual knife sharpener for less than $20.

Large pot: You'll need a pot that holds at least 8 quarts of liquid to make soups and stews.

Nonstick skillet: While I love a cast-iron skillet, I find that a nonstick skillet is so much handier. A nonstick surface means you won't need to add a lot of oil during cooking.

Nonstick baking sheet: A 13-by-9-inch nonstick baking sheet is perfect for roasting vegetables and baking cookies. (Parchment paper is great for creating a nonstick surface on baking sheets you already have and makes cleanup a breeze.)

Nonstick muffin pan: A nonstick or silicone muffin pan will help your healthy muffins slide right out—no need to worry about them sticking to the sides. It's good to have one 12-cup muffin pan and one mini muffin pan.

Vegetable peeler: Not only is a good peeler handy for prepping vegetables, but you can also use it to make vegetable noodles.

Blender: Whether you're whipping up sauces or just saving time chopping vegetables, a powerful blender makes prep work so much easier.

NICE-TO-HAVES

These items are optional, but they are still recommended to have.

Spiralizer: This handy tool makes it quick and easy to transform my vegetables into noodles. This is definitely optional, but fun!

Food processor: While a blender can be used for the recipes in this book, I love how quickly a food processor can chop onions, shred carrots, and finely mince garlic. You can even make your own nut butter in a food processor.

Cast-iron skillet: Cast-iron skillets tend to be an investment, but for good reason. They can literally last a lifetime, and they're great for uniform cooking temperatures. They can also go from the stovetop to the oven.

Rice cooker: A rice cooker makes it easy to prepare a big batch of not just rice but any grain without having to keep a close eye on it. I make a lot of quinoa, which cooks perfectly in a rice cooker.

Mandoline: A mandoline slicer makes it easy to cut produce into thin, uniform slices at a quick pace. It's handy for salads or dishes that require lots of sliced vegetables.

SHOPPING LIST

Grab your sustainable grocery bags, because we're going shopping for plant-based foods. When you decide to commit to a plant-based diet, a key component to your success is setting up your kitchen with all things plant-based.

The good news is that you'll still be shopping for the vegetables, fruits, and grains you've already been purchasing, but you need to leave the yogurt, eggs, and chicken sausage at the store. Get ready to load your cart with some of the nutritious foods listed below (seriously, do not buy everything on this list at once. You'll just be wasting precious produce if you do!). Happy shopping!

PLANT-BASED PROTEINS

Contrary to popular (and annoying) opinion, it isn't hard to get enough protein on a plant-based diet.

Soy Products
Edamame
Tofu
Tempeh

Nuts and Seeds
Almonds
Brazil Nuts
Cashews
Chia
Flaxseeds
Hazelnuts
Hemp seeds
Macadamia nuts
Pecans
Pine nuts

Pumpkin seeds
Sesame seeds
Sunflower seeds
Tahini (sesame seed butter)
Teff
Quinoa
Walnuts

Beans and Legumes
Adzuki beans
Black beans
Black-eyed peas
Chickpeas
Fava beans
Kidney beans
Lentils
Lima beans
Mung beans
Navy beans
Peanuts
Peas
Pinto beans
Split peas
String beans
White beans

Other
Wheat protein (seitan)
Soy, rice, hemp, or pea protein powders

CEREAL AND GRAINS

All grains are allowed on a plant-based diet, but complex carbohydrates are higher quality energy sources and contribute to better gut health. Try to stick with fiber-rich whole-grain options rather than refined flours.

Amaranth
Barley
Buckwheat
Bulgar
Cornmeal
Couscous
Farro
Freekeh
Kamut
Millet
Oats and oat bran

Orzo
Rice (white and brown)
Rye
Sorghum
Spelled
Wheatberries
White flour
Whole-wheat flour

VEGETABLES

There shouldn't be any restrictions on vegetables on any average plant-based diet.

Acorn squash
Artichoke hearts
Asparagus
Broccoli
Brussels sprouts
Cabbage
Carrots
Cauliflower
Celery

Cucumber
Eggplant
Mushrooms
Onions
Peppers
Radish
Spaghetti Squash
Tomatoes (yes, technically a fruit)
Turnips
Zucchini

Leafy Greens
Arugula
Bok choy
Collard Greens
Kale
Romaine
Spinach
Swiss Chard

Starchy Veggies
Beets
Butternut squash
Corn

Parsnips
Pumpkin
Sweet potato
Yam

FRUIT

Like vegetables, fresh fruits are one of the major pillars of a plant-based diet. Most varieties, like grapes and mangos, are higher in fructose than, berries, but unless you are really trying to watch your sugar intake, the natural kind in fresh fruit isn't much of an issue.

Apple
Avocados
Bananas
Cantaloupe
Cherries
Figs
Grapes
Jackfruit (great as a meat swap too!)
Mango

Peaches
Pears
Pineapple
Plums
Watermelon

Berries
Blueberries
Blackberries
Strawberries
Raspberries

Citrus
Grapefruit
Lemon
Lime
Orange
Tangerine

Dried Fruits
Apricots - Cranberries - Dates – Mango – Prunes - Raisins

PLANT-BASED OILS AND FATS

Butter is a no-no for a plant-based diet, but most plant-based oils are OK in moderation. If you're particular about how your oil is processed, avoid refined types and look for "expeller-pressed" or "cold-pressed" on the label.

Almond oil
Avocado oil
Canola oil
Coconut oil
Coconut butter
Grapeseed oil
Macadamia oil
Olive oil
Rice bran oil
Sesame oil

SWEETENERS

Several forms of sugar are okay on a plant-based diet. Having said that, here are some plant-based approved sweeteners.

Agave nectar
Beet Sugar
Brown rice syrup
Coconut sugar
Dates
Date syrup
Maple syrup
Raw cane sugar
Palm sugar
Stevia
Xylitol

HERBS AND SPICES

Herbs and spices are the ultimate weapons for adding flavour to your meals without resorting to processed condiments and unnecessary extra oil.

Basil
Chives
Cilantro
Cinnamon
Chili powder
Cumin
Dill
Garlic
Green onion
Ground ginger
Nutmeg
Oregano
Paprika
Parsley
Rosemary
Thyme
Turmeric

DRINKS

You have to say goodbye to dairy, however, these drinks will satisfy your need for something bubbly and smooth just as well.

Almond milk
Cashew milk
Coconut milk
Coconut water
Club soda
Kombucha
Macadamia nut milk

MISCELLANEOUS

Consider these foods if you require an extra boost in protein and vitamin intake, gut health, or mineral absorption.

- Seaweed (for protein): spirulina, kelp, and agar-agar

- Fermented foods (for gut-aiding bacteria, dairy-free,): natto, sauerkraut, miso paste, tempeh kimchi.
- Sprouted foods (for zinc absorption); nuts, sprouted beans, rice, lentils, bread, and quinoa.
- Nutritional yeast (for protein and vitamin B12)

SIMPLE MENU

SAMPLE MENU – 3 DAY MEAL PLAN

A plant-based diet includes nuts, vegetables, seeds, whole grains, fruits, tubers, and legumes with no animal products or processed foods. Check out our 3-day sample menu of plant-based delicious, recipes recommended to help you get started on the plant-based journey.

DAY 1

BREAKFAST

Oatmeal Breakfast Muffins

These moist hardy muffins feel just like eating a bowl of oatmeal.

Lunch

Vegan Sushi Power Bowl

This plant-based power bowl brings the sushi bar to your home.

Dinner

Perfect Lentil Soup with Mashed Potatoes

This rich and flavorful soup hits the spot-on chilly nights.

Snack

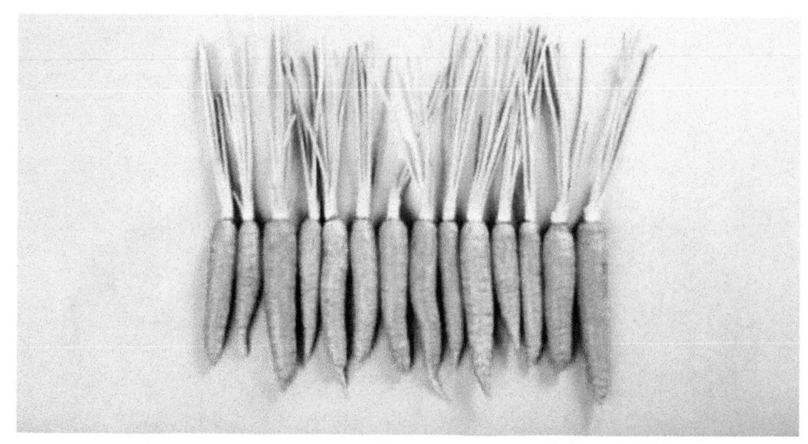

Carrots: What's Up Doc?

Three medium-sized carrots make an amazing snack!

DAY 2

Breakfast

3 Ingredient Pancakes

This simple and easy recipe has minimal ingredients and is so very good!

Lunch

Black Beans and Greens over Rice

Would quickly become your go-to meal as this is really satisfying.

Dinner

Quick & Easy Plant-Based Curry

Yummy, super nutritious, this curry ticks all the required boxes of a great meal!

Snack

Bananas: The Forbidden Fruit

Bananas make an easy to carry and very nutritious snack wherever you go.

DAY 3

Breakfast

Baked Steel Cut Oatmeal

Without any added sugar, every serving is sweet and nice.

Hearty Kale Salad

Nutrient-rich antioxidants packed delicious green salad.

Dinner

Black Bean Burger

Packed with fiber and protein, this burger is nutrient-rich.

Snack

Roasted Chickpeas

Great for a mid-afternoon snack.

A 7-DAY SAMPLE MENU FOR A STANDARD PLANT-BASED DIET

Day 1

Breakfast: Tofu scramble

Lunch: Cauliflower rice bowl with black beans, corn, avocado, and salsa

Dinner: Veggie-topped pizza

Snack: Zucchini chips

Day 2

Breakfast: Oatmeal-based breakfast muffins

Lunch: Tomato basil soup with oyster crackers

Dinner: Veggie stir-fry with tofu

Snack: Hummus wrap

Day 3

Breakfast: Homemade oatmeal bars

Lunch: Greek salad with a slice of whole-grain pita bread

Dinner: Kale and tofu curry

Snack: Cashew yogurt with berries and a scoop of peanut butter

Day 4

Breakfast: Breakfast burrito with eggs, peppers, and salsa

Lunch: Veggie burger and a side salad

Dinner: Cauliflower “steak” with roasted sweet potato fries

Snack: Veggies with hummus

Day 5

Breakfast: Dairy-free yogurt with berries and granola

Lunch: Tomato sandwich with pesto and a drizzle of olive oil

Dinner: Whole-wheat pasta with roasted tomatoes

Snack: Roasted chickpeas

Day 6

Breakfast: Chia seed pudding with fresh berries and a spoonful of almond butter

Lunch: Avocado toast

Dinner: Vegan mushroom enchiladas

Snack: Handful of almonds

Day 7

Breakfast: Oatmeal with almond milk

Lunch: Quinoa bowl with roasted carrots and sweet potatoes

Dinner: Vegetarian chili topped with slices of avocado

Snack: Whole-wheat toast topped with peanut butter (1)

RECIPES

ENERGY CHARGE/BREAKFAST

When you start with a healthy breakfast, it gives your body energy throughout the day. I find that if I eat healthy in the morning, I'm more likely to make healthy choices all day. Whether you're looking for something quick and easy to make on your way out the door or you need a healthy recipe that you can serve for brunch, these meals will keep you satisfied until lunchtime.

01- Banana Overnight Oats

SERVES 2; PREP TIME: 5 minutes, plus 6 hours to chill.

If your mornings always feel busy or chaotic, these overnight oats are for you. You can prep them the night before and then grab them to go on your way out the door. Customize them with your favorite toppings or keep things simple with a little peanut butter. The chia seeds help thicken up the oats overnight, but they also provide protein and fiber to keep you full and energized all morning long.

Ingredients:

- 1 banana
- 1 cup unsweetened almond milk
- 1 cup rolled oats
- 2 tablespoons chopped walnuts
- 2 tablespoons chia seeds
- 2 tablespoons maple syrup
- 1 teaspoon ground cinnamon
- 2 tablespoons peanut butter (optional)

Directions:

1. In a medium bowl, mash the banana with a fork. Add the almond milk, oats, walnuts, chia seeds, maple syrup, and cinnamon. Mash until combined.
2. Divide the mixture between two jars with tight-fitting lids.
3. Let chill in the refrigerator for at least 6 hours or overnight.
4. Top with the peanut butter (if using) just before serving.

Make-ahead tip: This recipe makes enough for two servings, but you don't have to eat them right away. Store the second jar for breakfast the following day!

Per serving: Calories: 332; Fat: 15g; Carbs: 50g; Fiber: 11g; Sugar: 20g; Protein: 9g; Sodium: 183mg

02- Grain-Free Granola

MAKES 2 CUPS [1/4 CUP = 1 SERVING], EQUIPMENT: Nonstick baking sheet
PREP TIME: 10 minutes, COOK TIME: 15 minutes

Store-bought granola is often loaded with sugar, unlike this super satisfying homemade version. Although the fat content might seem high, it's coming from the almonds and coconut, which provide protein and fiber. Plus, since it's low in sugar, you don't have to worry about an energy crash an hour later! This recipe is for 8 servings, so it's perfect for making ahead of time. Just store in an airtight container and scoop some out whenever you want to add a bit of crunch to your yogurt or oatmeal.

Ingredients:

- 3 tablespoons coconut oil
- 1/4 teaspoon pure vanilla extract
- 1 tablespoon honey
- 1 cup unsweetened coconut flakes

- 1 cup sliced almonds
- Pinch salt

Directions:

1. Preheat the oven to 300°F.
2. Pour the coconut oil into a small microwave-safe bowl and heat for 30 seconds, until melted, or melt in a small pan on the stovetop over low heat. Stir in the vanilla and honey.
3. In a large bowl, combine the coconut flakes, almonds, and salt. Drizzle with the coconut oil mixture and stir to coat.
4. Spread the granola in a single layer on a nonstick baking sheet. You can leave it a little chunky if you like clumps in your granola.
5. Bake for 10 to 12 minutes until the coconut begins to brown.
6. Let cool completely before removing from the baking sheet.

Per serving: Calories: 200; Fat: 18g; Carbs: 8g; Fiber: 4g; Sugar: 4g; Protein: 3g; Sodium: 24mg

03- Peanut Butter and Quinoa Breakfast Bowl

SERVES 2, EQUIPMENT: Medium saucepan, PREP TIME: 10 minutes, COOK TIME: 5 minutes.

If you love oatmeal, give this quinoa bowl a try. It has a similar flavor profile with a slightly different texture. Feel free to play around with additional toppings. Sometimes I trade the peanut butter and banana for cinnamon and raisins.

Ingredients:

- 1 cup cooked quinoa
- ¼ cup unsweetened almond milk
- 2 teaspoons honey
- ½ teaspoon pure vanilla extract
- 1 banana, sliced
- 2 tablespoons peanut butter

Directions:

1. In a medium saucepan over medium heat, combine the quinoa and almond milk and heat for 2 minutes.

2. Add the honey and vanilla and stir until combined.
3. Remove from the heat and divide between two bowls.
4. Top with the banana and peanut butter and serve.

Per serving: Calories: 307; Fat: 11g; Carbs: 45g; Fiber: 6g; Sugar: 16g; Protein: 10g; Sodium: 129mg

04- Pumpkin Almond Flour Muffins

MAKES 8 MUFFINS [1 MUFFIN = 1 SERVING]
EQUIPMENT: 8- or 12-cup nonstick muffin pan
PREP TIME: 10 minutes
COOK TIME: 25 minutes

If you've never baked with almond flour, try it with these muffins! Almond flour has just 24 grams of carbohydrates per cup, compared with 86 grams in whole-wheat flour. But although almond flour is low-carb, it's not low-calorie. If you want to lower the calorie count, leave out the pecans. Also, make sure you use plain pumpkin purée, not pumpkin pie filling, which has added spices and sugar.

Ingredients:

- ⅔ cup pumpkin purée
- 2 large eggs
- ¼ cup honey
- 1 tablespoon coconut oil, melted, at room temperature
- 1 teaspoon pure vanilla extract

- 1⅓ cups almond flour
- 1 teaspoon baking powder
- 1 teaspoon baking soda
- 1 teaspoon ground cinnamon
- ¼ teaspoon ground ginger
- ½ teaspoon salt
- ½ cup finely chopped pecans
- Nonstick cooking spray

Directions:

1. Preheat the oven to 350°F.
2. In a large bowl, combine the pumpkin purée and eggs. Mix in the honey, coconut oil, and vanilla.
3. In another large bowl, combine the almond flour, baking powder, baking soda, cinnamon, ginger, salt, and pecans.
4. Add the almond flour mixture to the pumpkin mixture and stir until just combined. The batter will be lumpy.
5. Spray a nonstick muffin pan with nonstick cooking spray. Evenly fill 8 muffin cups with the batter.
6. Bake for 19 to 22 minutes until browned on the edges and set in the middle.

7. Let sit for 2 minutes, then remove the muffins from the pan and cool on a cooling rack.

Prep tip: Be sure to remove the muffins from the pan. They can become soggy if left in the pan because the cups trap the escaping steam.

Per muffin: Calories: 150; Fat: 10g; Carbs: 13g; Fiber: 2g; Sugar: 10g; Protein: 4g; Sodium: 327mg

05- Greek Yogurt and Banana Muffins

MAKES 12 MUFFINS [1 MUFFIN = 1 SERVING], EQUIPMENT: 12-cup nonstick muffin pan, PREP TIME: 35 minutes, COOK TIME: 20 minutes

These banana muffins have an amazing fluffy texture, thanks to the Greek yogurt. You can substitute regular whole-wheat flour for the pastry flour, but pastry flour will result in a lighter muffin. As for the mix-ins, you can customize these with whatever you like. Nonstick cooking spray

Ingredients:

- 3 small or 2 large very ripe bananas
- ¼ cup honey
- 1 egg
- ¼ cup almond milk
- ½ cup plain Greek yogurt
- 1 teaspoon pure vanilla extract
- 1½ cups whole-wheat pastry flour
- 1 teaspoon baking soda

- 1 teaspoon baking powder
- ¼ teaspoon salt
- ½ cup chopped walnuts, cranberries, or dark chocolate chips (optional)

Directions:

1. Preheat the oven to 350°F. Spray a nonstick muffin pan with nonstick cooking spray.
2. In a large bowl, mash the bananas, then stir in the honey. Beat the egg into the mixture, then add the almond milk, yogurt, and vanilla.
3. In another large bowl, combine the flour, baking soda, baking powder, and salt.
4. Add the flour mixture to the banana mixture and stir until just combined. Be careful not to overmix. Add the walnuts, cranberries, or chocolate chips (if using).
5. Let the batter rest for 20 minutes.
6. Using a ¼-cup scoop, pour batter into each muffin cup.
7. Bake for 15 to 18 minutes or until the muffins are just starting to brown.
8. Let sit for 2 minutes, then remove the muffins from the pan and cool on a cooling rack.

Prep tip: It's important to let the batter rest to give the flour a chance to absorb the liquid. If you skip this step, your muffins will be dense and won't rise properly.

GLUTEN-FREE: Substitute any gluten-free flour for the whole-wheat pastry flour.

Per muffin: Calories: 65; Fat: 1g; Carbs: 14g; Fiber: 1g; Sugar: 9g; Protein: 2g; Sodium: 171mg

06- Greek Egg White Omelet

SERVES 2, EQUIPMENT: Large nonstick skillet, PREP TIME: 10 minutes, COOK TIME: 10 minutes

You can make an omelet out of all egg whites, but I prefer to use a couple of whole eggs for a fluffy and satisfying texture. Since feta has a strong flavor, you don't need a lot to make this breakfast really tasty.

Ingredients:

- 1 teaspoon olive oil
- ½ cup loosely packed spinach leaves
- ¼ cup diced red onion
- 2 garlic cloves, minced
- ¼ cup diced tomatoes
- 2 eggs
- 4 egg whites
- 2 tablespoons almond milk
- 2 tablespoons crumbled feta cheese

Directions:

1. Heat the olive oil in a large nonstick skillet over medium heat. Add the spinach, onion, and garlic, and cook for 2 to 3 minutes. Add the tomatoes and continue to cook for 2 minutes more, stirring occasionally.
2. In a small bowl, whisk together the eggs, egg whites, and almond milk.
3. Add the egg mixture to the skillet, tilting the pan to coat the spinach mixture with the eggs.
4. Cook for 2 to 3 minutes until the eggs are almost set, stirring gently so the eggs cook evenly and tilting the pan to let the softer parts of the egg mixture flow to the edges to cook.
5. Scatter the cheese over the top, and continue to cook for 1 to 2 minutes until the eggs are set but still moist.
6. Carefully fold the omelet in half, then cut into two pieces and serve.

DAIRY-FREE: Skip the feta and add a pinch of salt, if needed.

Per serving: Calories: 158; Fat: 9g; Carbs: 5g; Fiber: 1g; Sugar: 3g; Protein: 15g; Sodium: 241mg

07- Mini Egg Frittatas

SERVES 4, EQUIPMENT: 8- or 12-cup nonstick muffin pan, PREP TIME: 10 minutes COOK TIME: 25 minutes

These mini egg frittatas are a great low-carb breakfast option, and you can customize the fillings however you like. Swap out the onion and bell pepper for spinach and mushrooms for a different flavor.

Ingredients:

- Nonstick cooking spray
- 6 eggs
- ¼ cup diced yellow onion
- ¼ cup diced green bell pepper
- 2 tablespoons almond milk
- ¼ teaspoon garlic powder
- Pinch salt
- Pinch freshly ground black pepper
- 2 tablespoons shredded Parmesan cheese (optional)

Directions:

1. Preheat the oven to 350°F. Spray a nonstick muffin pan with nonstick cooking spray.
2. In a large bowl, whisk together the eggs, onion, bell pepper, almond milk, garlic powder, salt, pepper, and cheese (if using).
3. Pour the egg mixture evenly into 8 muffin cups.
4. Bake for 20 to 22 minutes until the eggs are set.
5. Let sit for 5 minutes before serving.

Flexitarian tip: Add ½ cup cooked ground turkey to the egg mixture before baking.

DAIRY-FREE: Skip the cheese and add 2 more tablespoons of diced bell pepper.

NUT-FREE: Substitute soy milk or dairy milk for the almond milk.

Per serving (2 mini frittatas):

Calories: 104; Fat: 7g; Carbs: 2g; Fiber: 0g; Sugar: 1g; Protein: 9g; Sodium: 143mg

08- Spicy Breakfast Tacos

SERVES 4, EQUIPMENT: Small saucepan, large nonstick skillet, PREP TIME: 15 minutes, COOK TIME: 15 minutes

Why save tacos for dinner? These mildly spicy tacos are great for breakfast or brunch, especially for a group. You can easily double the recipe to feed a crowd, and everyone can customize their taco with their favorite toppings.

Ingredients:

- 1 (15-ounce) can of black beans, drained and rinsed
- ½ teaspoon dried oregano
- ½ teaspoon ground cumin
- ½ teaspoon garlic powder
- ¼ teaspoon chili powder
- ¼ teaspoon salt, plus a pinch
- 8 eggs
- Hot sauce (optional)
- Pinch freshly ground black pepper
- 8 corn tortillas
- Nonstick cooking spray

- ½ cup pico de gallo or tomato salsa
- 1 avocado, sliced

Directions:

1. In a small saucepan, heat the black beans over medium heat. Add the oregano, cumin, garlic powder, chili powder, and ¼ teaspoon of salt. Cook for 5 to 7 minutes, stirring occasionally until heated through.
2. In a large bowl, beat the eggs with the hot sauce (if using). Add the remaining pinch of salt and pepper.
3. In a large nonstick skillet over medium heat, lightly toast the tortillas until they begin to brown, about 30 seconds on each side. Remove the tortillas and set them aside, covered by a kitchen towel.
4. Spray the skillet with nonstick cooking spray. Add the eggs and cook over medium-low heat until lightly set, scraping the pan frequently to keep them scrambled.
5. To assemble, top each tortilla with some of the scrambled eggs, black beans, pico de gallo or salsa, and avocado slices.
6. Sprinkle with more salt, pepper, and hot sauce, if desired.

Per serving (2 tacos): Calories: 306; Fat: 12g; Carbs: 32g; Fiber: 7g; Sugar: 2g; Protein: 19g; Sodium: 316mg

09- SAVORY SOUTHWESTERN BURRITOS

MAKES 6–7 BURRITOS

For those who like a more savory, salty breakfast, this burrito is our favorite. And as my sons can attest, these oh-so-good breakfast burritos can be served at any time of the day—breakfast, lunch, or dinner!

Ingredients:

- 4 large potatoes, diced
- Onion powder and sea salt, to taste
- 6–7 large whole grain tortillas
- 1 recipe Scrambled Tofu (page 82)
- 1 (15-ounce) can black beans, rinsed and drained
- 1 (15-ounce) jar salsa

Directions:

1. Preheat oven to 375°F.
2. Spread diced potatoes on a nonstick baking sheet. Season with onion powder and salt. After 15 minutes, flip the potatoes, then continue cooking for an additional 15–20 minutes.

3. Place 1/4 cup of potatoes in the center of each tortilla, top with 1/4 cup of the tofu mixture, then add 2 tablespoons of black beans.
4. Fold the bottom of the burrito over, then fold over both sides.
5. Place burritos, seam-side down, in a nonstick baking dish. Spread salsa across the top of burritos.
6. Bake for 10 minutes. Serve immediately.

10- SCRAMBLED TOFU

MAKES 4 SERVINGS

This simple scrambled tofu recipe can be spiced up with additional vegetables. For instance, my younger son likes to add 2–3 handfuls of spinach, kale, or other greens and serves it with diced potatoes, toast, and grits.

Ingredients:

- ½ large onion, diced
- ½ large carrot, grated
- 2 garlic cloves, minced
- 2 tablespoons vegetable broth
- 1 teaspoon curry powder
- 1½ teaspoons light miso
- 1 (14-ounce) package firm silken tofu, crumbled
- Sea salt and black pepper, to taste
- 8 chopped cherry tomatoes (optional)
- ¼ cup finely chopped kale (optional)

Directions:

1. In a nonstick pan, gently sauté onion, carrot, and garlic in vegetable broth over medium-high heat until onion browns.
2. Reduce heat to medium and add curry powder. Cook for 1–2 minutes, then add miso and tofu and cook for an additional 3–4 minutes.
3. Add salt and pepper. If desired, stir in cherry tomatoes and/or kale. Serve warm.

11- CASSAVA (YUCA) CON CEBOLLAS

MAKES 2–3 SERVINGS

From an early age, this easy, tasty dish was my younger son's favorite Dominican Garden recipe. Our favorite among the root crops is yuca (also known as cassava), which can be purchased in most supermarkets. It can be replaced with any potato or sweet potato, batata, breadfruit, plantain, or banana.

Ingredients:

- 4 cups chopped cassava
- 1 cup water
- 1 teaspoon salt, plus more to taste
- ½ cup chopped onions
- ½ cup diced tomatoes
- ¼ cup diced green bell peppers
- 2 teaspoons lime juice

Directions:

1. Peel cassava, then cut down the middle lengthwise. Place cassava face down on the cutting board and slice lengthwise one more time. Cut out the stiff fiber in the middle of the cassava, then chop into 1-inch cubes. You should have about 4 cups.
2. Place cassava in a pot and add water and salt. Cover and bring to a simmer over medium heat, then cook for about 30 minutes, until soft. Cooking time depends on the age of the cassava. Check every 2 minutes to see if it's soft, like a potato. When cooked, drain the liquid and set cassava aside.
3. In a skillet, combine onions, tomatoes, bell peppers, and lime juice and cook over medium-high heat for 1–2 minutes, until slightly soft. Do not overcook. Season with salt, then remove from the heat.
4. Place cassava on a serving plate and top with cooked vegetables. Serve warm.

12-Warm Quinoa Breakfast Bowl

SERVES 4 • PREP TIME: 5 MINUTES

I featured a bowl like this in the Boston episode of The Vegan Roadie. Loaded with protein, bright fruits, and savory nuts, this dish has all the textures and flavors I want to start my day off right. I hope it finds a spot in your breakfast lineup.

Ingredients:

- 3 cups freshly cooked quinoa
- 1⅓ cups unsweetened soy or almond milk
- 2 bananas, sliced
- 1 cup raspberries
- 1 cup blueberries
- ½ cup chopped raw walnuts
- ¼ cup maple syrup

Directions:

1. Divide the ingredients among 4 bowls, starting with a base of ¾ cup quinoa, ⅓ cup milk, ½ banana, ¼ cup raspberries, ¼ cup blueberries, and 2 tablespoons walnuts.

2. Drizzle 1 tablespoon of maple syrup over the top of each bowl.

Variations:

PROTEIN POWER BOWL: Add chia and hemp seeds for a protein-packed breakfast.

TROPICAL QUINOA BOWL: Replace the raspberries and blueberries with diced mango and pineapple and top with some unsweetened shredded coconut.

TIP: Make the quinoa ahead of time and warm it up in the microwave for a quick breakfast bowl.

LUNCH

13-Tofu and Veggies Buddha Bowl

Serving Size: 1
Servings per Recipe: 6
Calories: 957 calories per serving
Preparation Time: 10 minutes
Cooking Time: 40 minutes

Ingredients

- Sesame oil - 2 tablespoons
- Sweet mirin - 2 tablespoons

- Fiery Spice Blend - 1 tablespoon
- Kosher salt - 1 teaspoon
- Extra-firm tofu - 16 ounces
- Sweet potatoes (rinse and peel) – 2 medium
- Broccoli crowns - 2 medium
- Quinoa (cooked) - 1 kg
- Purple cabbage (thinly sliced) - 3 cups
- English cucumber (julienned) - 3 cups
- Avocado (thinly sliced) - 1 large
- Peanuts (roasted) - ⅓ cup
- Garnish
- Fresh cilantro leaves – 1 tablespoon
- Fresh mint leaf (torn) - 3 tablespoons
- Fiery peanut sauce
- Sesame oil - 2 tablespoons
- Apple cider vinegar - 2 tablespoons
- Fiery Spice Blend - 1 tablespoon
- Coldwater - ⅓ cup
- Kosher salt – as per taste

Directions

1. Start by preheating the oven by setting the temperature to 400 degrees Fahrenheit.

2. Now let us prepare the marinade for tofu. Take a medium-sized mixing bowl and add in the mirin, sesame oil, salt, and fiery spice blend. Mix well.

3. Toss in the tofu cubes and mix well. Ensure all cubes are well coated. Cover it using plastic wrap and place it in the refrigerator for about an hour.

4. Now take a large pot and fill it with cold water. Add salt and mix well. Toss in the sweet potatoes. Let it boil on medium-high flame.

5. Reduce the flame and let the sweet potatoes boil for 20 minutes.

6. Once done, remove the sweet potatoes from the water and set them aside. In the same water, blanch the broccoli florets for about a minute and a half.

7. Remove the broccoli and add transfer them to ice water. Let them sit in an ice bath for a minute. Remove and set aside on a plate lined with a paper towel. This will help in removing excess liquid.

8. Cut the boiled sweet potatoes lengthwise through the center. Further, cut into half-moon measuring 1 ½ -inch. Sprinkle with salt.

9. Take a baking sheet and grease it lightly. Place the sweet potato and marinated tofu onto the sheet.
10. Place it in the preheated oven and bake for about 20 minutes.
11. While the tofu and sweet potatoes are cooking. Let us prepare the fiery peanut sauce.
12. Take a medium mixing bowl and add in the apple cider vinegar, peanut butter, ¼ water, and spice blend. Whisk well to combine.
13. Now, let us assemble the 6 tofu and veggies Buddha bowls. For this, in a bowl add 1 cup of quinoa, then follow it with 2 ½ ounces of tofu, ½ a cup of sweet potato, ½ a cup of broccoli, ½ a cup of purple cabbage, ½ a cup of cucumber, and few slices of avocado.
14. Drizzle 2 tablespoons of peanut sauce and further top it with cilantro, mint, and crushed peanuts.

Nutrition Information

Fat – 28 g

Carbohydrates – 144 g / Protein – 39 g

14- Vegan Sheet Pan 3 Style Tofu

Serving Size: 1
Servings per Recipe: 4
Calories: 350 calories per serving
Preparation Time: 5 minutes
Cooking Time: 40 minutes (2-3 hours additional)

Ingredients

- Extra-firm tofu – 28 ounces
- Vegan barbeque sauce – as per taste
- Vegan teriyaki sauce – as per taste
- Tofu cutlets
- Soy sauce (low sodium) - 2 tablespoons
- Garlic powder (divided) - ¾ teaspoon
- All-purpose flour - ½ cup
- Corn starch - 1 tablespoon
- Non-dairy milk (unsweetened) - ½ cup

- Panko bread crumbs - ½ cup
- Nutritional yeast - 1 tablespoon
- Paprika - 1 teaspoon
- Cayenne pepper - ¼ teaspoon
- Kosher salt - ½ teaspoon
- Pepper - ¼ teaspoon
- Olive oil – as required

Directions

1. Start by preheating the oven by setting the temperature to 400 degrees Fahrenheit.
2. Take 2 tofu blacks and slice them through the center. Place all the blocks on the kitchen towel and cover with another. Place a baking tray and a heavy object to drain excess liquid. Let it sit for about an hour.
3. Take 2 tofu blocks and place them on a baking dish. Drizzle low-sodium soy sauce over each side evenly. Sprinkle gently with ¼ teaspoon of garlic powder on each side. Coat evenly. Let the tofu marinate for about 10 minutes.
4. Take a small mixing bowl and add in the cornstarch and flour. Mix well to combine. Take another bowl and pour in the milk.

5. Take a third mixing bowl and toss in the nutritional yeast, bread crumbs, paprika, cayenne pepper, remaining garlic powder, pepper, and salt. Mix well to combine.
6. Take the marinated tofu and coat it with a cornstarch mixture and then dip it in milk. Again coat it in cornstarch mixture, dip in milk, and finish by coating it with bread crumb and spice mixture.
7. Repeat the procedure with the second tofu block.
8. Take a baking dish and lightly grease it with olive oil. Place the tofu blocks and brush them using olive oil on each side.
9. Take the non-breaded tofu pieces and place them on the baking dish.
10. Take the teriyaki sauce and brush it on both sides of one non-breaded tofu piece.
11. Take the barbeque sauce and brush it on both sides of one non-breaded tofu piece.
12. Place the baking dish in the preheated oven and cook for about 15 minutes. Flip all four pieces and cook for another 15 minutes.

13. Remove the baking dish from the oven and transfer the tofu cutlets onto a wooden chopping board. Cut into cubes.
14. Serve them with salads or use them in sandwiches or wraps.
Note – These baked tofu cutlets can be stored in the refrigerator for up to 5 days.

Nutrition Information
Fat – 17 g
Carbohydrates – 28 g
Protein – 24 g

15-Buffalo Chickpeas and Lettuce Wraps

Serving Size: 1

Servings per Recipe: 2 Calories: 625 calories per serving

Preparation Time: 10 minutes

Cooking Time: 5 minutes

Ingredients

- Olive oil - 1 tablespoon
- Chickpeas - 1 can (15 ounces)
- Garlic powder - ½ teaspoon
- Salt - 1 pinch
- Buffalo sauce - ¼ cup
- Hummus - ⅓ cup
- Lemon juice - 1 tablespoon

- Water - 1 tablespoon
- Tortillas - 2 large
- Romaine lettuce – 4 leaves
- Red onion (sliced)
- Tomato (sliced)

Directions

1. Take a large nonstick saucepan and pour 1 tablespoon of olive oil. Place it over medium flame.
2. Once the oil starts simmering, toss in the chickpeas and cook for about 3 minutes.
3. Add in the salt, buffalo sauce, and garlic powder. Cook for about 2 minutes. The sauce should be thick and coat the chickpeas well. Keep aside.
4. Take a small mixing bowl and add in the hummus, water, and lemon juice. Whisk well to combine.
5. Now take the tortillas and place 2 romaine lettuce leaves in the center. Top it with chickpeas, sliced tomatoes, and sliced red onions.
6. Pour the hummus dressing on top.
7. Fold the edges and roll it in the shape of a burrito. Cut in equal halves.

8. Repeat the process with the other tortilla.

Nutrition Information

Fat – 19 g

Carbohydrates – 89 g

Protein – 25 g

16- Lentil and Cheese Nuggets

Serving Size: 1

Servings per Recipe: 6

Calories: 217 calories per serving

Preparation Time: 10 minutes (3 hours additional)

Cooking Time: 20 minutes

Ingredients

- Lentils - 1 ½ cups
- Carrot (sliced) - 1
- Corn - ½ cup
- Pea - ½ cup
- Vegan cheddar cheese (shredded) - 1 cup
- Dried oregano - 1 teaspoon
- Salt - 1 teaspoon
- Pepper - 1 teaspoon
- Red pepper flakes - ½ teaspoon
- Garlic - 1 clove

Directions

1. Start by soaking the lentil for 3 hours in cold water.
2. Once the lentils are done soaking, set the temperature of the oven at 400 degrees Fahrenheit and let it preheat.
3. Take a baking tray and line it using parchment paper.
4. Now take a food processor and add in the carrots, peas, corns, vegan cheddar cheese, salt, oregano, pepper, garlic, soaked lentils, and red pepper flakes. Pulse to mix all the ingredients well.
5. Form nuggets by taking 1 tablespoon of lentil mixture using your hands. Repeat the process with the rest of the mixture.
6. Place all the nuggets onto the lined baking tray. Bake for about 10 minutes. Flip over and bake for another 10 minutes.
7. Remove the baking tray from the oven and let the cutlets rest for about 5 minutes. Serve!

Nutrition Information

Fat – 7 g

Carbohydrates – 24 g; Protein – 13 g

17-Black Bean and Sweet Potato Burritos

Serving Size: 1, Servings per Recipe: 3

Calories: 542 calories per serving
Preparation Time: 10 minutes
Cooking Time: 30 minutes

Ingredients

- Sweet potatoes (peel and cut in cubes) - 2 medium Olive oil – as per taste
- Smoked paprika - ½ teaspoon
- Garlic powder - ½ teaspoon
- Kosher salt – as per taste
- Pepper – as per taste
- Yellow onion (diced) - ½ medium
- Jalapeño (diced) - ½ medium
- Garlic (minced) - 1 clove

- Chili powder - 1 teaspoon
- Ground cumin - ½ teaspoon
- Cayenne pepper – as per taste
- Black beans (drain and rinse) - 1 can (15 ounces) Corn - ¾ cup
- Flour tortillas - 3 large
- Lettuce leaves (chopped) – for serving
- Tomato (diced) – for serving
- Vegan cheddar cheese (shredded) - for serving Guacamole - for serving

Directions

1. Start by preheating the oven by setting the temperature to 400 degrees Fahrenheit.
2. Take a nonstick baking tray and toss in the cubed sweet potatoes. Drizzle olive oil on top. Also sprinkle the garlic powder, paprika, pepper, and salt. Toss well to ensure the sweet potatoes are evenly coated.
3. Place the tray in the preheated oven and bake for about 10 minutes. Flip over the sweet potatoes and bake for another 10 minutes.
4. Take a nonstick saucepan and drizzle olive oil. Place it over medium flame.
5. Once the oil starts simmering, toss in the onions and cook for about 4 minutes.

6. Add in the garlic, jalapeno, cumin, cayenne pepper, and chili powder. Cook for another 3 minutes.
7. Toss in the black beans, pepper, and salt and cook for 3 minutes. The ingredients should completely heat through.
8. Let us now assemble the burrito, place one of the tortillas on a flat surface. Add 1/3 of corn and bean mixture, 1/3 of prepared sweet potatoes, a little bit of lettuce, guacamole, diced tomatoes, and vegan cheddar cheese in the center. Fold in the edges and roll to form a burrito. Repeat the process of the remaining tortillas.
9. Cut each burrito into two equal halves and serve.

Nutrition Information

Fat – 12 g
Carbohydrates – 95 g
Protein – 16 g

18- Mac and Peas and Cashew Sauce

Serving Size: 1

Servings per Recipe: 4

Calories: 567 calories per serving

Preparation Time: 10 minutes

Cooking Time: 10 minutes

Ingredients

- Yellow potatoes (peel and cut in cubes) -2
- Carrot (peel and cut in 1-inch pieces) - 1 medium onion (peel and cut in 4 quarters) - 1
- Cashews - ½ cup
- Salt - 1 teaspoon
- Garlic powder - 1 teaspoon
- Onion powder - 1 teaspoon
- Nutritional yeast - 2 tablespoons
- Macaroni (cooked) - 16 ounces
- Green peas - 2 cups
- Paprika – as per taste

Directions

1. Start by taking a large pot with water and place it over high heat. When it comes to a boil add in the carrots, onions, and potatoes. Cover the pot with a lid and boil for about 10 minutes.

2. Remove the boiled vegetables using a strainer. Reserve about 2 cups of water for later use.

3. Take a blender and add in the boiled carrots, onions, potatoes, cashews, salt, garlic powder, onion powder, nutritional yeast, paprika along with the reserved water. Blend well to form a smooth puree like consistency.

4. Place the cooked macaroni in a large mixing bowl and pour the prepared puree on top. Toss in the green peas and mix well. Serve!

Nutrition Information

Fat – 7 g

Carbohydrates – 105 g
Protein – 21 g

19- Chickpea, Mango and Curried Cauliflower Salad

Prep Time: 10 minutes
Cook Time: 25 minutes
Total Time: 35 minutes
Servings: 4

Ingredients

- 1 teaspoon curry powder
- 1 teaspoon sugar
- 1 teaspoon ground mustard
- 1 teaspoon ground coriander
- ½ teaspoon ground turmeric
- ½ teaspoon ground cumin
- 3 tablespoons olive oil more as needed

- 1 medium yellow onion thinly sliced
- 1 cup canned chickpeas drained, rinsed, and warmed through slightly
- 1 head of cauliflower cut into 1-inch florets, blanch for 2 minutes in boiling water, and then pat dry
- 2 large mangoes peeled, pitted, and chopped into ½-inch pieces
- 1 jalapeno stemmed, seeded, and diced small
- 1 cup chopped cilantro
- 2 tablespoons lime juice
- 2 cups baby spinach
- 1 cup baby arugula
- Salt and black pepper

Direction

1. Blend the curry powder, cinnamon, ground mustard, coriander, cumin, ½ teaspoon of kosher salt, and ¼ teaspoon black pepper in a small bowl. Set it aside.

2. Put the olive oil in a large skillet. Add the onion and cook at high heat for about 6 minutes. Attach the mixture of spices and turn the heat to medium-low. Cook an extra 6 minutes. Move to a wide bowl and add to the same bowl the chickpeas. Keep the pan at medium heat.

3. Add the cauliflower to the same pan where the onion was cooked. If required, add more olive oil. Cook in the remaining spice mixture for about 5 minutes or until the cauliflower is seasoned and cooked clean. Use the onion and chickpeas to transfer the cauliflower to the bowl. Let sit for approximately 20 minutes at room temperature.

4. Apply the pineapple, jalapeno, coriander, lime juice, spinach, and arugula to the dish. Toss to disperse the ingredients evenly. Adjust seasoning to taste and serve as soon as possible.

5. Enjoy!

Nutrition Information

Fat – 10 g

Carbohydrates – 13 g

Protein – 19 g

20- Vegetable and Tofu Skewers

Serving Size: 1
Servings per Recipe: 4
Calories: 187 calories per serving
Preparation Time: 10 minutes (1 hour additional)
Cooking Time: 17 minutes

Ingredients

- Water - ½ cup
- Maple syrup - ¼ cup
- Soy sauce - 3 tablespoons
- BBQ sauce - 2 tablespoons
- Oil - 1 tablespoon
- Garlic powder - 1 tablespoon
- Sriracha - 1 tablespoon
- Black pepper - 1 teaspoon

- Firm tofu - 15 ounces
- Peppers - 2
- Onions – 2 medium
- Zucchini - 1
- Skewers - 4

Directions

1. Start by taking a shallow dish and fill it with water. Soak the wooden skewers in the same as this will prevent them from burning.
2. Take the zucchini and slice it into round slices. Also, cut peppers and onions in squares.
3. In the meanwhile, take a quarter plate and line it with a paper towel. Place tofu and cover it with another paper towel and place a plate on top.
4. Place the tofu along with plates in the microwave for about 3 minutes.
5. Remove the tofu and place it on a chopping board. Cut it into cubes.
6. Take a glass measuring cup and add in the water, soy sauce, maple syrup, oil, barbeque sauce, pepper, Sriracha, and garlic powder. Stir well.

7. Take a rectangle storage box and place the tofu inside it. Pour the prepared sauce over tofu and cover it with a lid. Place it in the refrigerator for about an hour.
8. Once done, remove the tofu from the marinade. Keep aside
9. Take a nonstick saucepan and pour the marinating liquid into the saucepan. Place it over low flame for about 10 minutes. Put off the flame once the sauce starts to thicken.
10. Remove the skewers from the water and start assembling them.
11. Take 1 skewer and start assembling by alternating between zucchini, onion, pepper, and tofu.
12. Take a grill pan and place it on medium flame. Cook each assembled skewer on each side for about 4 minutes. Glaze each side with sauce while cooking.
13. All sides should have a light char as this will add a nice smoky flavor to the dish.

Nutrition Information

Fat – 9 g
Carbohydrates – 17 g
Protein – 11 g

21-Baked deep-dish apple pancake

Makes: one 8-to 9-inch (20 to 23 cm) pancake; Serves 6 to 8

TIME: 10 minutes to prep, 30 to 35 minutes to bake

Ingredients

- 4 tart apples (such as Gala, Honeycrisp, or Granny Smith), peeled, cored, and thinly sliced
- ¼ cup (30 g) chopped walnuts or pecans, optional
- 1 teaspoon ground cinnamon
- 1½ cups (225 g) whole wheat flour
- 2 teaspoons baking powder
- ¼ teaspoon plus 1/8 teaspoon salt

- 1 cup (240 ml) light or full-fat coconut milk
- 2 tablespoons maple syrup
- 1 tablespoon plus 1 teaspoon fresh lemon juice
- 1 teaspoon vanilla extract
- ¼ cup (35 g) unpacked dark brown sugar or coconut sugar
- 1 tablespoon coconut oil

Preparation

1. Preheat the oven at 190 ° C (375 ° F). Place on medium heat a deep cast-iron skillet. Once warm, add in a single layer the apples, ½ teaspoon cinnamon, and walnuts if used. Let the apples cook while the batter is being cooked.
2. In a medium bowl, combine the flour, baking powder, ¼ teaspoon salt, and ½ teaspoon cinnamon remaining. Stir the coconut milk, maple syrup, 1 tablespoon of lemon juice, and vanilla together in a separate bowl, then pour into the dry ingredients and whisk until mixed.

3. Sprinkle the sugar, 1 teaspoon of lemon juice leftover from the apples, and 1/8 teaspoon of salt. Remove from the heat, apply the coconut oil to the pan, concentrating on the apples ' perimeter.

4. Spoon the batter over the top and bake for 30 to 35 minutes, until the pancake is golden brown and cooked through. Slice into wedges, pick and serve on bowls.

Nutrition Information

Fat – 17 g

Carbohydrates – 103 g

Protein – 83 g

22- *Black Bean and Veggie Soup*

Serving Size: 1
Servings per Recipe: 6
Preparation Time: 10 minutes
Cooking Time: 45 minutes

Ingredients

- Olive oil - 2 tablespoons
- Onion (diced) - 1
- Celery stalks (chopped) - 2
- Carrot (chopped) - 1
- Red bell pepper (diced) - 1
- Garlic (minced) - 4 cloves
- Jalapeño (seeded and diced) - 1
- Salt - 1 teaspoon

- Pepper - 1 teaspoon
- Cumin - 2 tablespoons
- Black beans (drained and rinsed) – 4 cans (60 ounces) Vegetable stock - 4 cups
- Bay leaf – 1
- For serving
- Avocado (chopped)
- Queso fresco (crumbled)
- Fresh cilantro (chopped)
- Tortilla chip (crumbled)

Directions

1. Start by taking a stockpot (large) and place it over a high flame. Add in the oil and reduce the heat the medium-high.
2. Once the oil starts to shimmer, toss in the onions, carrot, bell peppers, and celery.
3. Let the veggies cook for about 5 minutes. Keep stirring.
4. Now add in the minced garlic, pepper, and salt. Cook for about 10 more minutes. The veggies should be tender by now.
5. Add in the vegetable stock, black beans, bay leaf, and cumin.

6. Bring the ingredients to a boil and reduce the flame to low. Cover the stockpot with a lid and cook for about 30 minutes. Beans should also be tender by now.
7. Take a blender and transfer 4 cups of the beans and vegetable soup into the same. Blend into a smooth puree like consistency.
8. Pour the blended vegetables and beans into the stockpot. Mix well to combine. This will help in thickening the soup.
9. Let the soup simmer over low flame for another 10 minutes.
10. Once done, garnish with queso fresco, avocado, tortilla chips, and chopped cilantro.

Nutrition Information

Fat – 6 g
Carbohydrates – 49 g
Protein – 17 g

23- Spinach Pasta in Pesto Sauce

Serving Size: 1

Servings per Recipe: 2

Calories: 591 calories per serving

Preparation Time: 20 minutes
Cooking Time: 15 minutes

Ingredients

- Olive oil - 1 tablespoon
- Spinach - 5 ounces
- All-purpose flour - 2 cups
- Salt - 1 tablespoon plus ¼ teaspoon (keep it divided) Water - 2 tablespoons
- Roasted vegetable for serving
- Pesto for serving
- Fresh basil for serving

Directions

1. Take a large pot and fill it with water. Place it over a high flame and bring the water to a boil. Add one tablespoon of salt
2. While the water is boiling, place a large saucepan over a medium flame. Pour in the olive oil and heat it through.
3. Once the oil starts to shimmer, toss in the spinach and sauté for 5 minutes.
4. Take a food processor and transfer the wilted spinach. Process until the spinach is fine in texture.
5. Add in the flour bit by bit and continue to process to form a crumbly dough.
6. Further, add ¼ tsp of salt and 1 tbsp of water while processing to bring the dough together. Add the remaining 1 tbsp of water if required.
7. Remove the dough onto a flat surface and sprinkle with flour. Knead well to form a dough ball.
8. Use a rolling pin to roll out the dough. The dimensions of the rolled dough should be 18 inches long and 12 inches wide. The thickness should be about ¼ - inch thick.

9. Cut the rolled dough into long and even strips using a pizza cutter. Make sure the strips are ½ - inch wide.
10. The strips need to be rolled into evenly sized thick noodles.
11. Toss in the prepared noodles and cook for about 4 minutes. Drain using a colander.
12. Transfer the noodles into a large mixing bowl and add in the roasted vegetables, pesto. Toss well to combine.
13. Garnish with basil leaves.

Nutrition Information

Fat – 8 g
Carbohydrates – 110 g
Protein – 16 g

24- Vegan Alfredo Fettuccine Pasta

Serving Size: 1
Servings per Recipe: 2
Calories: 844 calories per serving
Preparation Time: 15 minutes
Cooking Time: 15 minutes

Ingredients

- White potatoes - 2 medium
- White onion - ¼
- Italian seasoning - 1 tablespoon
- Lemon juice - 1 teaspoon
- Garlic - 2 cloves
- Salt - 1 teaspoon
- Fettuccine pasta - 12 ounces
- Raw cashew - ½ cup

- Nutritional yeast (optional) - 1 teaspoon
- Truffle oil (optional) - ¼ teaspoon

Directions

1. Start by placing a pot on high flame and boiling 4 cups of water.
2. Peel the potatoes and cut them into small cubes. Cut the onion into cubes as well.
3. Add the potatoes and onions to the boiling water and cook for about 10 minutes.
4. Remove the onions and potatoes. Keep aside. Save the water.
5. Take another pot and fill it with water. Season generously with salt.
6. Toss in the fettuccine pasta and cook as per package instructions.
7. Take a blender and add in the raw cashews, veggies, nutritional yeast, truffle oil, lemon juice, and 1 cup of the saved water. Blend into a smooth puree.
8. Add in the garlic and salt.
9. Drain the cooked pasta using a colander. Transfer into a mixing bowl.
10. Pour the prepared sauce on top of the cooked fettuccine pasta. Serve.

Nutrition Information

Fat – 13 g

Carbohydrates – 152 g

Protein – 28 g

25- Tempeh Vegetarian Chili

Prep: 5 minutes
Cook: 25 minutes
Total: 30 minutes
Servings: 4

Ingredients

•2 tablespoons of olive oil 30 mL
•1 8-oz package tempeh 226 g, roughly grated
•1 medium white onion diced
•1 red bell pepper diced
•1 stalk celery diced
•2 cloves garlic minced
•3/4 cup tomato sauce 177 mL
•1 15-oz can kidney beans 425 g, drained
•1 15-oz can black beans 425 g, drained

•1 cup water 240 mL
•1 tablespoon of cumin
•¼ tablespoon of each chili powder and crushed red pepper flakes
•To serve: chopped green onions, plain Greek yogurt

Preparation

1. Brown Tempeh: warm the oil in a large pot over medium/high heat. Attach the tempeh and cook for about 5 minutes until lightly browned. It's all right if some of it sticks to the pan's bottom. Once you add the fluids, it'll come off.
2. Add Flavor Makers: add onion, pepper bell, celery, and garlic, cook until veggies are slightly soft, about 5 minutes.
3. Prepare Everything: add the remaining ingredients, reduce heat to medium, and prepare for about 15 minutes until hot and mixed. Taste the seasonings and change them as needed. Complete and serve with green onions.

Nutritional info

•Serving: 1serving
•Calories: 522kcal
•Carbohydrates: 64g
•Protein: 30g
•Fat: 22g
•Sodium: 1900mg
•Fiber: 17g

26- Healthy Lentil Soup

Total Time: 15 minutes
Number of servings: 6

Ingredients:

- 1 ½ teaspoon vegetable oil
- 2 medium carrots, sliced
- 1 ½ onion, chopped
- 1 ½ cups dry brown lentils, rinsed, soaked for about 2 hours
- 3 bay leaves
- 2 tablespoons lemon juice or to taste
- 6 cups vegetable broth
- ½ teaspoon dried thyme
- Salt to taste
- Pepper to taste

Directions:

1. Place a soup pot over medium heat. Add oil. When the oil is heated, add onions and sauté until translucent.
2. Add the rest of the ingredients except lemon juice and stir.
3. When it begins to boil, lower the heat and cover it with a lid. Simmer until the lentils are tender.
4. Add lemon juice and stir.
5. Ladle into soup bowls and serve.

Nutritional values per serving:

Calories – 230, Fat – 3 g, Carbohydrate – 33 g, Fiber –15.6 g, Protein – 18.7g

27- Lentil Vegan Soup

Serving Size: 1

Servings per Recipe: 5

Calories: 364 calories per serving

Ingredients

- Olive oil - 2 tablespoons
- Onion (diced) - 1
- Garlic (minced) - 2 cloves
- Carrot (diced) - 1
- Potatoes (diced) - 2
- Tomato (diced) - 1 can (15 ounces)
- Dried lentil - 2 cups
- Vegetable broth - 8 cups
- Bay leaf - 1
- Cumin - ½ teaspoon

- Salt – as per taste
- Pepper – as per taste

Directions

1. Start by taking a large pot and add in 2 tablespoons of olive oil. Place the pot over medium flame.
2. Once the oil heats through, toss in the onions and cook for 5 minutes.
3. Add in the garlic and cook for another 2 minutes.
4. Now toss in the diced potatoes and carrots. Sauté for about 3 minutes.
5. Add the remaining ingredients like vegetable broth, tomatoes, lentils, cumin, and bay leaf.
6. Once it comes to a boil, reduce the flame to low and cook for about 40 minutes.
7. Remove the bay leaf and season with pepper and salt.
8. Transfer into a serving bowl. Serve hot!

Nutrition Information

Fat – 7 g

Carbohydrates – 58 g

Protein – 19 g

28- Chickpea and Avocado Salad

Serving Size: 1

Servings per Recipe: 4

Calories: 399 calories per serving

Preparation Time: 15 minutes

Cooking Time: 0 minutes

Ingredients

- Dressing
- Olive oil - 2 tablespoons
- Lime juice - ¼ cup
- Cumin - 2 teaspoons
- Chili powder - 2 teaspoons
- Salt - 1 teaspoon
- Pepper - 1 teaspoon
- Fresh cilantro (chopped) - ¼ cup

- Salad
- Chickpeas (rinsed and drained) - 2 cans
- Cucumber (quartered and chopped) - 1
- Cherry tomatoes (cut in half) - 20
- Onion (chopped) - 1
- Avocado (diced) - 1
- Carrot (shredded) – 1/3 cup

Directions

1. Start by preparing the dressing. For this, take a small mixing bowl and add in the olive oil, lime juice, cumin, chili powder, salt, pepper, and fresh cilantro.
2. Whisk well until all ingredients are well combined. Keep aside.
3. Take a large mixing bowl and toss in the chickpeas, tomatoes, cucumber, onion, carrots, and avocado.
4. Pour the dressing over the salad and toss well using your hands or salad spoons. Ensure all ingredients are evenly combined.
5. Transfer onto salad bowl and serve!

Nutrition Information

Fat – 12 g

Carbohydrates – 57 g; Protein – 18 g

29- *Roasted Vegetables and Lentil Salad*

Serving Size: 1
Servings per Recipe: 2
Calories: 569 calories per serving
Preparation Time: 30 minutes

Ingredients

- Butternut squash (cubed) - 2 cups
- Brussels sprouts (quartered) - 2 cups
- Red onion (cut in wedges) - 1
- Olive oil - 1 tablespoon
- Salt – as per taste
- Pepper - as per taste
- Green lentil (rinsed) - 1 cup
- Water or vegetable broth - 3 cups
- Balsamic vinegar - 3 tablespoons
- Maple syrup - 1 tablespoon

Directions

1. Start by preheating the oven by setting the temperature to 400 degrees Fahrenheit.
2. Take a baking dish and line it with parchment paper, Toss in the butternut squash, red onions, and Brussels sprouts. Generously season with salt, pepper, and olive oil. Mix well using your hands and ensure all ingredients are well coated.
3. Place the tray in the baking tray in the oven and bake for 10 minutes. Flip the veggies and bake for another 10 minutes.
4. Take a medium nonstick saucepan and place it over a high flame. Add in the water/vegetable broth and lentils.
5. Once it comes to a boil, cover the pan with a lid and let it simmer for about 25 minutes. Drain any excess water and keep it aside.
6. Take a large mixing bowl and empty the roasted vegetables. Also, transfer the cooked lentils to the mixing bowl.
7. To prepare the dressing, take a liquid measuring cup and add in the balsamic vinegar, pepper, salt, and maple syrup. Whisk well to combine.

8. Pour the prepared dressing over roasted vegetables and lentils. Toss well to make sure all ingredients are well coated.
9. Transfer into 2 bowls and serve.

Nutrition Information

Fat – 8 g
Carbohydrates – 102 g
Protein – 28 g

30- Quinoa Salad Southwestern Style

Serving Size: 1
Servings per Recipe: 2
Calories: 873 calories per serving
Preparation Time: 5 minutes
Cooking Time: 22 minutes

Ingredients

- Vegetable oil - 2 tablespoons
- Garlic (minced) – 3 cloves
- Jalapeño (minced) - 1
- Black beans - 15 ounces
- Corn - 15 ounces
- Roma tomatoes (diced) - 3
- Quinoa (rinsed) - 1 cup
- Vegetable stock - 2 cups

- Chili powder - 1 tablespoon
- Cumin - 2 teaspoons
- Salt - 1 teaspoon
- Pepper - 1 teaspoon
- Avocado (cubed) - 1 teaspoon
- Lime (juiced) - 1
- Fresh cilantro (for garnishing)

Directions

1. Start by placing a large saucepan on medium flame.
2. Toss in the minced jalapeno and garlic. Cook for about a couple of minutes.
3. Add in the corn, black beans, quinoa, tomatoes, chili powder, vegetable stock, pepper, and salt.
4. Cover the saucepan with the lid and cook for about 20 minutes. Quinoa should be tender and should have absorbed the liquid.
5. Mix gently using a wooden spoon.
6. Take a large serving bowl and empty the quinoa into the same. Pour lime juice and gently mix.
7. Garnish with avocado and cilantro.

Nutrition Information: Fat – 23 g; Carbohydrates – 143 g; Protein – 33 g

31-Easy bean burritos

Preparation time: 3 minutes
Cooking time: 1 minute
Number of servings: 2

Ingredients

- 1½ cups (390 g) Slow-Cooker Refried Beans
- 1 large sweet potato, cubed and roasted or steamed
- ½ cup (30 g) nutritional yeast
- ½ cup (120 g) salsa 12 (8-inch or 20 cm) wholegrain tortillas
- 1 cup (245 g) hummus or 1 cup (240 ml)

Direction

1. Drain from the sautéed vegetables some excess liquid. In a pan, add the peas, sautéed

onions, sweet potatoes, nutritional yeast, and salsa. Put it aside.

2. Using tortillas, hummus, bean mixture, and 12 pieces of parchment paper or aluminum foil to set up an assembly line on the fridge.

3. Warm the tortillas one at a time. (Microwave them for about 15 seconds each, or bake them for 5 to 7 minutes at 350 ° F/180 ° C wrapped in a wet, lint-free towel.)

4. Lay hummus on a hot tortilla, then top with ½ cup (90 g) of the bean-vegetable mixture. Roll, first pull the bottom and top in, then the sides in. Wrap the parchment or foil securely. Continue and top with the leftover tortillas. Enable cooling, then cooling for up to 5 days or freezing for up to 2 months.

Nutrition Information

Fat – 12g

Carbohydrates – 63 g

Protein – 33 g

32- Sweet Potato, Spinach & Butter Bean Stew

Servings: 12 (can easily be halved)
Ready in: 45 Minutes

Ingredients

- 1.25 kg sweet potatoes
- 260g young leaf spinach
- 4 x 400g can chopped tomatoes
- 2 x 400g can butter beans
- 4 garlic cloves (crushed)
- 2 medium onions (finely chopped)
- 2 tablespoons of olive oil
- 2 tablespoons of ground cumin
- 2 tablespoons of ground coriander
- 3 tablespoons of smoked paprika

- 500ml vegetable stock
- Juice of 1 to 2 lemons
- Large bunch of fresh coriander
- Salt & pepper

Preparation

1. Cut and slice sweet potatoes in 1 cm dice (0.40 inch).
2. In a large pot, warm olive oil.
3. Fine-cut onion, split garlic, ground cumin, ground coriander, and smoked paprika. Cook until tender is the onion.
4. Include sweet potatoes, tomatoes chopped, and stock.
5. Take to the boil and cook until sweet potatoes are soft (they should still have a bite).
6. Cut the spinach. Cook for about 2 minutes. Add butter beans that have been rinsed and drained. Cook to warm them up for another 2 minutes.
7. Season with lemon juice, salt, and pepper to taste.
8. Serve with plenty of fresh ground leaves of chopped coriander.

Nutrition Information: Fat – 19 g; Carbohydrates – 43 g; Protein – 23 g

SNACKS, DESSERT

33- BANANA WALNUT MUFFINS

Makes 12 Muffins

Bananas in my household never go to waste, even when they are soft and overripe. If I'm not freezing them for my favorite Chocolate Cravings, I'm using them in this recipe. Taking only 10 minutes to prepare, these muffins are scrumptious with the addition of chopped walnuts.

Ingredients

- 2 cups whole wheat pastry flour
- 1 teaspoon baking powder
- 1 teaspoon baking soda
- 1 teaspoon ground cinnamon
- ¼ cup raw cane sugar
- ¼ cup chopped walnuts
- 2 ripe bananas
- 1 cup unsweetened nondairy milk (rice, soy, almond, etc.)
- Topping
- ¼ cup raw cane sugar
- ½ teaspoon ground cinnamon

Preparation

1. Preheat oven to 350°F.
2. Line a 12-cup muffin tin with paper liners (or use a nonstick pan).
3. Combine flour, baking powder, baking soda, cinnamon, sugar, and walnuts in a medium-size mixing bowl.
4. In a separate bowl, mash bananas and milk together.
5. Fold dry ingredients into the wet mixture. Spoon the mixture into the muffin cups.
6. For the topping, mix together sugar and cinnamon in a small bowl. Sprinkle on top of muffins.
7. Bake for 20–25 minutes, until a toothpick inserted into the center of a muffin comes out clean.

34- BLACKBERRY LEMON TEA CAKES

MAKES 12 TEA CAKES

Picking blackberries and making pies, cobblers, and lemon tea cakes are fond summertime memories of childhood. This delectable berry is one of our favorite fruits, and it adds a wonderful addition to these tasty lemon tea cakes.

Ingredients

- 2 cups whole wheat pastry flour
- ½ cup raw cane sugar

- 1½ teaspoons baking powder
- 1½ teaspoons grated lemon zest
- 1¼ cups unsweetened nondairy milk (rice, soy, almond, etc.)
- 1 tablespoon lemon juice
- 1 cup blackberries
- 2 tablespoons unsweetened shredded coconut

Preparation

1. Preheat oven to 350°F. Line a baking sheet with parchment.
2. Combine flour, sugar, baking powder, and zest in a medium-size mixing bowl.
3. In a separate bowl, mix together milk and lemon juice.
4. Fold dry ingredients into the wet mixture, then gently add the blackberries. Do not overmix.
5. Place 1–2 tablespoons of mixture on a lined baking sheet, repeating until mixture is gone. Top with coconut.
6. Bake for 20–25 minutes, until a toothpick inserted into the center of a tea cake comes out clean.

35- PUMPKIN PIE MUFFINS WITH PECANS

MAKES 12 MUFFINS

On the go, after school, or on the way to soccer practice, you'll find that these muffins make a great snack. And what's better, they take only about 10 minutes to prepare and 20–25 minutes to bake.

Ingredients

- 2 cups whole wheat pastry flour
- ½ cup raw cane sugar
- 1 teaspoon baking powder
- 1 teaspoon baking soda
- 1 teaspoon ground cinnamon
- ½ teaspoon ground ginger
- ½ teaspoon ground nutmeg
- ½ teaspoon ground allspice
- ¼ teaspoon salt
- ½ cup pumpkin puree
- 1 cup water
- ½ cup applesauce
- ½ cup whole pecans

Preparation

1. Preheat oven to 350°F.
2. Line a 12-cup muffin tin with paper liners (or use a nonstick pan).
3. Combine flour, sugar, baking powder, baking soda, cinnamon, ginger, nutmeg, allspice, and salt in a medium-size mixing bowl.
4. In a separate bowl, mix together pumpkin puree, water, and applesauce.
5. Fold dry ingredients into the wet mixture. Spoon mixture into muffin cups.
6. Gently press a few pecans onto the top of each muffin.
7. Bake for 20–25 minutes, until a toothpick inserted into the center of a muffin comes out clean.

36- FIESTA CORNBREAD

MAKES 6 SERVINGS

Made with fresh corn kernels, this cornbread is great with hearty stews, beans, and collard greens.

Ingredients

- 1 cup cornmeal
- 1 cup whole wheat pastry flour
- 1 teaspoon baking powder
- 1 teaspoon baking soda
- ½ teaspoon sea salt
- ½ teaspoon dried tarragon
- ¾ cup corn, fresh off the cob
- ⅓ cup unsweetened applesauce
- 2 tablespoons maple syrup
- 1⅓ cups unsweetened nondairy milk (rice, soy, almond, etc.)

Preparation

1. Preheat oven to 350°F.
2. Combine cornmeal, flour, baking powder, baking soda, salt, and tarragon in a medium-size mixing bowl.
3. In a separate bowl, mix together corn, applesauce, maple syrup, and milk. Add to the dry ingredients and mix.
4. Pour into a 9 x 9-inch nonstick baking dish (or baking dish lined with parchment).
5. Bake for 30–35 minutes, until a toothpick inserted into the center of the cornbread comes out clean.

37- LEMON POPPY MUFFINS

MAKES 12 MUFFINS

Nutty and pleasant-tasting, poppy seeds are a wonderful addition to bread, rolls, bagels, and cakes. And for those who have a sweet tooth, try one of the fruit butter with this recipe.

Ingredients

- 2 cups whole wheat pastry flour
- ¼ cup poppy seeds
- 1 teaspoon baking powder
- 1 teaspoon baking soda
- 1 teaspoon grated lemon zest
- ½ cup raw cane sugar

- 1 cup unsweetened nondairy milk (rice, soy, almond, etc.)
- 1/4 cup lemon juice

Preparation

1. Preheat oven to 350°F.
2. Line a 12-cup muffin tin with paper liners (or use a nonstick pan).
3. Combine flour, poppy seeds, baking powder, baking soda, lemon zest, and raw cane sugar in a medium-size mixing bowl.
4. In a separate bowl, mix together milk and lemon juice.
5. Fold dry ingredients into the wet mixture. Spoon the mixture into the muffin cups.
6. Bake for 20–25 minutes, until a toothpick inserted into the center of a muffin comes out clean.

38- POTATO ROLLS

MAKES 12 ROLLS

My grandmother believed a meal was not complete without bread, and I would blissfully enjoy at least 3 or 4 of her potato rolls. She used oil and dairy, so I've adapted the recipe to make my own tasty and easy version of Granny's famous potato rolls.

Ingredients

- 2¼ cups whole wheat pastry flour
- 1 teaspoon salt

- 2 teaspoons instant (rapid-rise) yeast
- 1 cup warm unsweetened non-dairy milk (rice, soy, almond, etc.)
- 1½ tablespoons maple syrup
- 6 tablespoons cooked mashed potatoes

Preparation

1. In a large bowl, combine flour and salt. Set aside.
2. In a separate bowl, mix together yeast, milk, and maple syrup. Set aside for 5–10 minutes, until light foam forms.
3. Make a well in the center of the flour and pour in the wet mixture and mashed potatoes. Mix together until a soft dough forms. Place dough on the counter and knead for 1–2 minutes.
4. Divide dough into 12 rolls. Place rolls in a 9 x 13-inch nonstick baking pan (touching is fine). Cover and leave in a warm, draft-free place to double about 1 hour.
5. Preheat oven to 350°F.
6. Uncover and bake for 20–25 minutes, until golden brown.

39- SENSATIONAL HERB BREAD

MAKES 1 LOAF

Once you make this bread, you'll want to make it again and again. Simple and tasty, it goes well with lots of different entrées, as well as soups, salads, and sandwiches. My family loves savory bread, and this is one of our favorites.

Ingredients

- 2¼ cups whole wheat pastry flour
- 2 teaspoons onion powder

- 1½ teaspoons dried oregano
- 1 teaspoon dried rosemary
- 1 teaspoon dried basil
- ½ teaspoon sea salt
- 2 teaspoons instant (rapid-rise) yeast
- 1 cup warm water
- 1 teaspoon molasses

Preparation

1. In a large bowl, combine flour, onion powder, oregano, rosemary, basil, and salt. Set aside.
2. In a separate bowl, mix together yeast, water, and molasses. Set aside for 5–10 minutes, until light foam forms.
3. Make a well in the center of the flour and pour in the wet mixture. Mix together until a soft dough forms. Place dough on the counter and knead for 1–2 minutes.
4. Transfer the dough to an 8 x 4-inch nonstick bread pan and cover. Leave in a warm, draft-free place to double, about 1 hour.
5. Preheat oven to 350°F.
6. Uncover and bake for 30–35 minutes. Bread is done when it sounds hollow when tapped on the top with your knuckles

40- FRENCH APPLE PIE BREAD

MAKES 1 LOAF

Ingredients

- 2 cups whole wheat pastry flour
- 1 teaspoon baking powder
- ½ teaspoon baking soda
- 1 teaspoon ground cinnamon
- ½ teaspoon ground nutmeg
- ½ teaspoon ground ginger
- ¼ teaspoon salt
- 1¼ cups unsweetened nondairy milk (rice, soy, almond, etc.)
- ½ cup maple syrup
- 1 teaspoon vanilla extract

- 1 cup peeled and shredded apples
- ½ cup chopped walnuts
- 1 cup raisins
- ¼ cup rolled oats

Preparation

1. Preheat oven to 350°F.
2. In a large bowl, combine flour, baking powder, baking soda, cinnamon, nutmeg, ginger, and salt.
3. In a separate bowl, combine milk, maple syrup, and vanilla. Add to dry ingredients.
4. Fold in apples, walnuts, and raisins. Do not overmix.
5. Spread into a 9 x 9-inch nonstick baking pan and sprinkle with oats. Bake for about 45 minutes, until a toothpick inserted into the center, comes out clean.

DINNER

41- Mexican Street Salad

Total Time: 10 minutes
Number of servings: 5

Ingredients:

- 5 medium radishes, trimmed, finely sliced
- 1 small white cabbage, shredded
- ¼ small red cabbage, shredded
- ¼ cup extra-virgin olive oil
- 4 carrots, peeled, finely sliced
- Handful cilantro, finely chopped
- 4 large jalapeno chilies or to taste, finely sliced

- 2 red onions, peeled, finely sliced
- ½ cup lime juice
- Sea salt to taste

Directions:

1. Add all the ingredients in a bowl except the red cabbage. Toss well.
2. Add the red cabbage just before serving.

Nutritional values per serving:

Calories – 111,
Fat – 6.5 g,
Carbohydrate – 9.24 g,
Fiber – 4.2 g,
Protein – 2.2 g

42- Almond Crunch Chopped Kale Salad

SERVES 4 • PREP TIME: 10 MINUTES • COOK TIME: 10 MINUTES

I love this salad because I can put it together quickly and it's loaded with flavor. I make the dressing first, so it is ready to go by the time my salad ingredients are prepared, and I can avoid the apple oxidizing
and turning brown. This is one of my favorite dishes to take to a Fourth of July gathering; there are never any leftovers! My recipe calls for Lacinato kale, also known as Tuscan or dinosaur kale. It's the one with the darker, narrower, flat leaves.

INGREDIENTS FOR THE DRESSING

- ¼ cup tahini
- 2 tablespoons Dijon mustard
- 2 tablespoons maple syrup
- 1 tablespoon lemon juice
- ¼ teaspoon salt

INGREDIENTS FOR THE ALMOND CRUNCH

- ½ cup finely chopped raw almonds

- 2 teaspoons soy sauce or gluten-free tamari
- 1 teaspoon maple syrup
- ¼ teaspoon sea salt

INGREDIENTS FOR THE SALAD

- 1 bunch Lacinato kale, stemmed and roughly chopped
- 1 green apple, cored and thinly sliced

Preparation

1. Preheat the oven to 325°F. Line a baking sheet with parchment paper.
2. To make the dressing: Whisk together all the dressing ingredients in a small bowl and set aside.
3. To make the almond crunch: Mix together all the almond crunch ingredients in a medium bowl and spread out evenly on the prepared baking sheet. Bake for 5 to 7 minutes, until slightly darker in color and crunchy. Let cool for 3 minutes.
4. To make the salad: In a large bowl, mix together the kale and apples. Toss with the dressing and top with the almond crunch.

VARIATIONS

TOFU-KALE TAHINI WRAP: Add some Basic Baked Tofu, throw it into a wrap with this salad, and you have a complete lunch! The wrap holds up nicely even with the dressing because the Lacinato kale is so sturdy.

SALTED CHOPPED KALE TOAST: Avocado toast is popular, but pile this on top of your toast and sprinkle it with some flaked sea salt to wow your brunch guests.

TIP: If you want to slice the apples in advance, toss them in the juice of ½ lemon to keep them from browning.

43- Cobb Salad with Portobello Bacon

SERVES 4 • PREP TIME: 15 MINUTES

This salad offers up a combination of fresh ingredients that complement one another and bring out the best of what's in the garden. Top with some decadent ranch and the added crisp of bacon for a light lunch that won't leave you hungry.

Ingredients

- 2 heads romaine lettuce, finely chopped
- 1-pint cherry tomatoes halved
- 1 avocado, peeled, pitted, and diced
- 1 cup frozen (and thawed) or fresh corn kernels
- 1 large cucumber, peeled and diced
- Portobello Bacon or store-bought vegan bacon
- 4 scallions, thinly sliced
- Unhidden Valley Ranch Dressing or store-bought vegan ranch dressing

Preparation

1. Scatter a layer of romaine in the bottom of each of the 4 salad bowls. With the following ingredients, create lines that cross the top of the romaine, in this order: tomatoes, avocado, corn, cucumber, and portobello bacon.
2. Sprinkle with the scallions and drizzle with ranch dressing.

VARIATIONS

CHICKEN COBB SALAD: Use your favorite vegan chicken, cut into ½-inch cubes, as an additional line on top of the lettuce.

PROTEIN COBB SALAD: Punch up the protein by adding some beans, hemp seeds, or chia seeds—or all three!

TIP: I like to keep a batch of Portobello Bacon on hand to put on salads, sandwiches, and pizzas. Most of the time it doesn't make it into any recipe, though, as I find myself munching on it as a snack.

44- Vegan Greek Meatball Soup

Preparation time: 10 minutes
Cooking time: 50 – 60 minutes
Number of servings: 4

Ingredients:

- ¾ cup dry brown lentils, rinsed, soaked in water for a couple of hours if possible
- ½ small onion, chopped
- 2 ½ cups vegetable broth
- Juice of a large lemon
- 2 tablespoons breadcrumbs
- Salt to taste
- Pepper to taste
- 7 tablespoons long-grain brown rice
- ¼ cup flour
- ½ tablespoon cornstarch mixed with 2 tablespoons water
- 2 tablespoons chopped parsley
- 1 tablespoon olive oil
- 1 tablespoon ground flaxseeds
- 2 cups water
- ¼ cup flour
- Olive oil, to drizzle

Directions:

1. Place a saucepan over medium-high heat. Add 2 cups of broth and lentils into the saucepan.
2. When it begins to boil, reduce the heat to medium heat and simmer until lentils are cooked. Place a wire mesh strainer over a bowl and strain the lentils. Retain the cooking water.
3. Place another small saucepan with 6 tablespoons of rice and remaining broth over medium heat. Cook until rice is soft. Turn off the heat.
4. Add the retained lentil cooked liquid back to the saucepan. Add water and place over medium heat.
5. Meanwhile, add lentils and half the cooked into the food processor bowl and pulse until coarsely mashed.
6. Transfer into a bowl. Add remaining cooked rice, parsley, oil, breadcrumbs, and flaxseeds and mix until well combined.
7. Divide the mixture into 12 equal portions and shape it into balls. Place flour on a plate. Dredge the balls in flour.

8. Add the remaining tablespoon of uncooked rice to the simmering broth and drop the lentil balls into it.
9. Reduce heat and simmer for about 30 minutes.
10. Add cornstarch mixture to the simmering broth and stir gently. Add lemon juice, salt, and pepper, and mix well.
11. Ladle into soup bowls. Trickle some olive oil on top and serve.

Nutrition Information

Calories – 461.8, Fat – 5.75 g, Carbohydrate – 51.6 g, Fiber – NA, Protein – 20 g

45- Irish "Lamb" Stew

Preparation time: 10 minutes
Cooking time: 50 – 60 minutes
Number of servings: 4

Ingredients:

- ½ cup Textured vegetable protein (TVP) chunks or soy chunks
- Salt to taste
- Pepper to taste
- 3 cloves garlic, minced
- 2 stalks celery, chopped
- 2 potatoes, peeled, chopped into chunks
- 1 ½ - 2 ½ cups vegetable stock
- ½ tablespoon minced fresh rosemary
- 2 tablespoons all-purpose flour
- 1 medium onion, chopped
- 1 cup button mushrooms or cremini mushrooms, halved or quartered depending on the size of the mushrooms

- 1 medium carrot, cut into thin, round slices
- ¼ bottle beer or ¼ cup wine
- ½ tablespoon minced, fresh thyme
- 1 tablespoon vegetable oil

Directions:

1. Add TVP into a bowl of hot water and let it soak for 30-40 minutes. Drain and set aside for 5-7 minutes.
2. Add flour, salt, and pepper into a bowl and stir. Roll the TVP chunks in the flour mixture. Shake the chunks to drop off extra flour. Set aside the remaining flour mixture.
3. Place a soup pot over medium heat. Add 2 teaspoons of oil and heat.
4. Add TVP and stir. Cook until brown all over.
5. Remove with a slotted spoon and place on a plate lined with paper towels.
6. Add ½ teaspoon oil into the pot. When the oil is heated, add garlic, salt, pepper, and onion and sauté until onions are pink.
7. Add vegetables and herbs and mix well.
8. Add the retained flour mixture and sauté for 1-2 minutes.

9. Stir in the TVP, beer, and stock. Stir constantly until it begins to boil.
10. Lower the heat and cover with a lid. Cook until tender. Stir occasionally.
11. Add more water or stock if you like to dilute the stew.
12. Season with salt and pepper.
13. Ladles into bowls and serve.

Nutrition Information

Calories – 229, Fat – 4 g, Fiber – 9.3 g, Protein – 17.2 g

46- Cauliflower Fried Rice

Cook time: 30 mins
Servings: 4
Ingredients

- 1 lb. (450 g) tofu
- 1/2 cup (150 g) peas, fresh or frozen 1 tablespoon ginger, minced
- 3 garlic cloves, minced
- 1/4 cup (30 g) green onions, sliced 1 cauliflower head, riced
- 2 carrots, diced
- 2 tablespoons sesame oil
- 3 tablespoons cashews
- 3 tablespoons soy sauce, or tamari sesame seeds, for garnish

Direction:
1. Press and drain the tofu. Then crumble it slightly in a bowl. Set aside.
2. Add oil to a wok pan and place over medium heat. Add the garlic and ginger and cook until slightly brown and fragrant, for about 1 minute.

3. Add the tofu and stir for about 6 minutes, until golden and well cooked. Set the tofu aside.
4. Add more oil to the pan and add the carrots. Sauté for about 2-3 minutes until tender.
5. Add the peas along with the cauliflower rice and stir until combined. Cook for about 6-8 minutes, until the cauliflower becomes tender.
6. Add the green onions, cooked tofu, cashews, and soy sauce
7. Serve the cauliflower fried rice and garnish with the sesame seeds.

Enjoy!

47- Sesame Tofu Veggies

Cook time: 30 mins
Servings: 4
Ingredients
Noodles:

- 6 oz (170 g) brown rice vermicelli, or rice noodles 1/4 teaspoon red pepper flakes
- 1 teaspoon lime juice or lemon
- 1/2 teaspoon toasted sesame oil

Sticky Sesame Tofu:

- 1 teaspoon oil
- 14 oz (400 g) firm tofu, pressed, drained, and cubed 1 hot Chile, green or red
- 1/2 cup (64 g) carrots, shredded
- 2 teaspoon sesame oil
- 2 bell peppers, sliced
- 1 tablespoon cornstarch
- 1/2 cup (125 ml) water
- 1 tablespoon ginger, minced
- 1/3 cup (82 ml) soy sauce or tamari 1 cup (100 g)

Mixed veggies:

- 5 garlic cloves, chopped

- 3 teaspoon sriracha
- 1 tablespoon orange juice
- 1/4 cup (65 ml) maple syrup
- 3 tablespoons rice vinegar
- Salt and pepper, to taste

Direction

1. Cilantro, toasted sesame seeds, and pepper flakes, for garnish, Prepare the noodles and per the package instructions. Drain, rinse and add to a bowl. Add in the lemon juice, sesame oil, and pepper flakes and stir.
2. Add oil to a skillet and place over medium heat. Add the cubed tofu and cook for 5-8 minutes until slightly brown. Transfer to a bowl.
3. Add the peppers, sesame oil, veggies, and Chile pepper to the skillet, cook for extra 4 minutes.
4. Add the ginger and garlic, cook for 3-4 minutes. Add the sauce ingredients, salt and mix well to combine. Add the crisped tofu and allow the mixture to boil for 4-5 minutes.

5. Add the cornstarch to a bowl along with water and mix well to combine. Pour the cornstarch slurry into the pan and cook until the sauce has thickened. Adjust the seasonings. Add the coconut sugar or cayenne. Serve the mixture in separate bowls and add pepper flakes, sesame seeds, and cilantro. Enjoy!

48- Cauliflower Steaks

Cook time: 25 mins Servings: 4

Ingredients

- 1 cauliflower
- 2 tablespoons parsley, chopped
- 2 tablespoons pine nuts, toasted 1 tablespoon cooking oil
- 1 tablespoon golden raisins
- Salt and pepper, to taste
- ½ teaspoon lemon zest
- Romesco Sauce:
- 2 bells peppers, fresh or frozen 2 tablespoons red wine vinegar
- 3 tablespoons water
- ¼ cup (30 g) almonds, blanched
- 2 tablespoons tomato paste
- 1 teaspoon sweet paprika
- 2 garlic cloves

- ¼ cup cooked chickpeas
- ¼ cup hazelnuts, toasted
- ¼ cup (65 ml) olive oil
- Salt and pepper, to taste

Direction

1. Prepare the sauce by combining the tomato paste, red peppers, vinegar, chickpeas, water, almonds, hazelnuts, paprika, garlic, olive oil, salt, and pepper in a blender, and process until smooth.
2. Preheat the oven to 400 F/200 C. Slice the cauliflower into thick steak pieces, leave the core intact.
3. Add oil to a pan, and add the cauliflower steaks. Brush the steaks with a little oil and season with salt and pepper. Sear each side for 3 minutes until lightly brown.
4. Then place on the baking sheet and bake for 13-15 minutes.
5. Serve the steaks with the sauce. Top with pine nuts, lemon zest, chopped parsley, raisins. Enjoy!

49- Mexi Walnut and Sun-Dried Tomato Lettuce Wraps

SERVES 4 • PREP TIME: 15 MINUTES

Said the walnut to the sun-dried tomato, "Lettuce get together." And so they shall. I love this mixture of sweet and tangy sun-dried tomatoes with the earthy and fruity flavor of the walnuts; with just a few spices and accompanying veggies, the combination can't be beaten! This recipe comes together in a snap for an anytime meal or snack.

Ingredients:

- 1 cup walnuts, roughly chopped
- ½ cup sun-dried tomatoes, roughly chopped (rinsed if packed in oil)
- 2 carrots, peeled and grated
- 1 celery stalk, thinly sliced
- ¼ cup roughly chopped fresh cilantro
- 2 teaspoons Taco Seasoning or store-bought taco seasoning
- Juice of ½ lime
- 2 teaspoons olive oil
- 2 teaspoons agave or maple syrup

- Sea salt
- 6 to 12 Bibb lettuce leaves
- 2 scallions, thinly sliced

Preparation:

1. In a large bowl, toss together the walnuts, sun-dried tomatoes, carrots, celery, cilantro, taco seasoning, lime juice, oil, and agave. Mix well to combine. Season with salt, starting with just a couple pinches and adding more if desired.
2. Scoop some of the mixtures onto each lettuce leaf. Sprinkle with scallions and serve.

VARIATIONS

DESSERT LETTUCE WRAPS: Omit the walnuts, sun-dried tomatoes, carrots, celery, cilantro, and taco seasoning (the first 6 ingredients). Instead, use 1 cup roughly chopped mango, 1 cup hulled and roughly chopped strawberries, and ¼ cup roughly chopped fresh basil. Mix with the lime juice, olive oil, and agave in a large bowl until well combined. Divide among the lettuce leaves and dust with organic confectioners' sugar.

TOFU LETTUCE WRAPS: Omit the walnuts and sun-dried tomatoes. Instead, use 1 (14-ounce block) extra-firm tofu, drained and crumbled. Mix with the remaining ingredients in a large bowl, divide among the lettuce leaves and sprinkle with the scallions.

TIP: Make all three variations for a party and leave the different fillings in bowls for guests to build their own wraps.

50- Kaledit Salt and Vinegar Kale Chips

SERVES 2 • PREP TIME: 5 MINUTES • COOK TIME: 10 MINUTES

Kale chips have come and gone; they were very popular and now seem to be forgotten. But I always keep this recipe in my back pocket. It's super simple and is still the life of the party when I put these chips out at gatherings. My kale chips bring all the boys to the yard!

Ingredients:

- 1 large bunch curly kale, stemmed and torn into 2- to 3-inch pieces (about 4 cups)
- 2 tablespoons apple cider vinegar
- 1 tablespoon olive oil
- ¾ teaspoon sea salt

Preparations:

1. Preheat the oven to 350°F. Line a large baking sheet or 2 small baking sheets with parchment paper.

2. Combine all the ingredients in a large bowl and massage everything together for 1 to 2 minutes, until the kale is soft and a darker green.
3. Spread the kale in a single layer on the prepared baking sheet(s). Do not pile the pieces on top of each other. Bake for 8 to 10 minutes, until the kale is crunchy.
4. Cool before serving. Store leftovers in a sealed container for up to 1 week.

VARIATIONS

DESSERT KALE CHIPS: Omit the vinegar. Add 1 teaspoon vanilla extract, 1 teaspoon organic cane sugar, and ½ teaspoon ground cinnamon. Toss well to combine.

CHEESE KALE CHIPS: Omit the vinegar. Add 2 tablespoons of Walnut Parmesan.

TIP: After washing kale, dry it very thoroughly before dressing with the oil and vinegar (a salad spinner might help). Kale that is wet from the water will not crisp up in the oven.

51- Simple Spinach and Artichoke Flatbread

SERVES 6 • PREP TIME: 10 MINUTES • COOK TIME: 15 MINUTES

There is a pizza place in New York City called Artichoke Basile's that always has a long line out the door. I finally waited my turn one day and got a slice, and it was a slice of heaven. When I went vegan, I vowed to figure out a way to replicate that slice without all the cholesterol—or the use of a pizza oven. The original slice didn't have mushrooms, but I couldn't resist topping off this concoction of creamy goodness with some baby Bellas!

Ingredients:

- 1½ cups raw cashews, soaked overnight or boiled for 10 minutes, and drained
- 1½ cups water
- Juice of 1 lemon
- 2 garlic cloves, roughly chopped
- 1½ teaspoons onion powder
- 1½ teaspoons sea salt

- 1 (14-ounce) can quartered artichokes, rinsed, drained, and roughly chopped
- 1 (10-ounce) bag frozen spinach, thawed, drained, and squeezed dry
- 6 (6-inch) whole-wheat pita bread
- 6 teaspoons olive oil, divided
- 1 (8-ounce) package baby bella mushrooms, stemmed and sliced (optional)
- Walnut Parmesan or store-bought vegan Parmesan, for garnish
- Red pepper flakes, for garnish

Preparation:

1. Preheat the oven to 350°F. Line two baking sheets with parchment paper.
2. Combine the cashews, water, lemon juice, garlic, onion powder, and salt in a blender and blend until smooth. Pour the cashew mixture into a large mixing bowl. Add the artichokes. Now, double-check that your spinach is really and truly dry because it will make your mixture watery if not. Then add the spinach and mix until well combined.

3. Brush each pita with 1 teaspoon of olive oil. Lay the pitas on the prepared baking sheets. Spread ½ cup of the spinach and artichoke mixture on each pita and top with the sliced baby bellas, if using.

4. Bake for 15 minutes, or until the edges start to turn golden brown. Top each flatbread with Parmesan and red pepper flakes.

VARIATIONS

CLASSIC SPINACH-ARTICHOKE DIP: Turn this into the life of the party! Bake the cashew and artichoke mixture in an oven-safe baking dish at 350°F for 25 minutes and top with Walnut Parmesan. Serve with crispy tortilla chips or warm bread.

MINI PIZZAS: Using burrito-size tortillas, cut out rounds with a 2½-inch biscuit cutter or round cookie cutter. Spray a muffin tin with nonstick cooking spray. Place a tortilla round in each muffin cup and top with a heaping tablespoon of the spinach-and-artichoke mixture. Bake at 350°F for 12 minutes. Remove from the oven and pop out each mini pizza with a fork. Sprinkle with Walnut Parmesan and red pepper flakes. Keep them coming, because your guests will devour these.

TIP: If you don't have a brush to brush the oil over the pitas, drizzle the olive oil over the pitas and spread it with a clean paper towel.

52- GGB Bowl

SERVES 2 • PREP TIME: 10 MINUTES • COOK TIME: 5 MINUTES

Here it is, my beloved grains, greens, and beans bowl. Feel free to tweak it as you will; this recipe is open to interpretation and personal preference. Use it to expand your ingredient knowledge, knowing that you can count on a complete protein at the end each time!

Ingredients

- 2 teaspoons olive oil
- 1 cup cooked brown rice, quinoa, or your grain of choice
- 1 (15-ounce) can chickpeas or your beans of choice, rinsed and drained
- 1 bunch spinach or kale, stemmed and roughly chopped
- 1 tablespoon soy sauce or gluten-free tamari
- Sea salt
- Black pepper

Preparations

1. In a large skillet, heat the oil over medium heat. Add the rice, beans, and greens and stir continuously until the greens have wilted and everything is heated for 3 to 5 minutes.
2. Drizzle in the soy sauce, mix to combine, and season with salt and pepper.

VARIATIONS

ROASTED VEGETABLE BOWL: Add roasted vegetables to your GGB bowl. Use 1 cup sliced carrots and 1 zucchini, halved and sliced, for some color. Toss with 1 tablespoon olive oil and salt and pepper to taste, and roast at 400°F for 20 minutes, tossing the vegetables halfway through.

PROTEIN POWER GGB BOWL: Add a vegan protein like tofu, tempeh, or another meat alternative to the bowl. Sprinkle with hemp and/or chia seeds for a protein-packed meal.

TIP: Be adventurous and mix and match to your liking. Make it as is at first, and then let your creative side explore and expand. Find a new green you want to try? Use that. A bean you have always been curious about? Use that. Always wanted to make that pot of couscous? Now is the time! It's your kitchen and your bowl, so take charge and make food that piques your palate.

53- Red, White, and Green Pasta Bowl

SERVES 6 • PREP TIME: 10 MINUTES • COOK TIME: 15 MINUTES

I have such a love-hate relationship with pasta. Carbs tend to do that to us, eh? When I was a kid, one of my favorite meals was a big bowl of spaghetti loaded with butter and processed Parmesan cheese. Thankfully, I've grown to love my vegetables as an adult, but even better, I find joy mixing them into my pasta. So I'm eliminating the hate and making it a big old bowl of love! I hope you can do the same with this recipe, where veggies, beans, and kale join pasta bow ties.

Ingredients

- 1 tablespoon olive oil
- 1 onion, chopped
- ½ cup roughly chopped sun-dried tomatoes
- 1 (8-ounce) package baby bella or white button mushrooms, stemmed and sliced
- 6 garlic cloves, minced

- ¼ teaspoon sea salt
- ¼ teaspoon black pepper
- ¼ teaspoon red pepper flakes
- ½ cup low-sodium vegetable broth
- 1 bunch kale, stemmed and roughly chopped
- 3 cups farfalle, cooked
- 1 (15-ounce) can cannellini beans, rinsed and drained
- Walnut Parmesan or store-bought vegan Parmesan, for garnish (optional)
- Chopped fresh parsley, for garnish (optional)

Preparation

1. Heat the oil in a large skillet over medium heat. Add the onion, sun-dried tomatoes, and mushrooms and sauté until the onion is soft and the mushrooms have reduced in size, about 5 minutes. Add the garlic, salt, black pepper, and red pepper flakes and cook for 1 additional minute, or until fragrant.

2. Slowly add the broth to the pan and stir in the kale. Cover and simmer for 5 minutes, or until the kale is completely wilted.
3. Stir in the cooked pasta and beans and cook for 2 minutes, or until heated through.
4. Serve in shallow bowls and garnish with Parmesan and chopped fresh parsley, if desired.

VARIATIONS

SAUSAGE FARFALLE BOWL: Omit the mushrooms. Add 3 links of your favorite vegan Italian sausage, sliced, for a heartier dish or to satiate your carnivorous friends.

MARINARA AND FARFALLE: This dish is intended to be a drier pasta. Add your favorite store-bought sauce or Magnificent Marinara if you prefer more gravy with your pasta.

TIP: Sun-dried tomatoes that are packed in oil are fine for this—just take out the number of tomatoes you need and rinse them off. For a flavor boost, use 1 tablespoon of the oil from the jar of tomatoes instead of the olive oil called for in the recipe.

54- The Cabbage Patch Bowl

SERVES 4 • PREP TIME: 10 MINUTES • COOK TIME: 25 MINUTES

The Cabbage Patch Dance, the Cabbage Patch Kids, and now . . . the Cabbage Patch Bowl! Cabbage has always seemed a forgotten ingredient to me. I look at it and think, “What can you do for me, cabbage?” The truth is that it’s very adaptable and goes well with everything! In this recipe, I pair it with a couple of my favorite veggies and my all-time favorite dressing. I hope it brings a smile to your face as it does to mine.

Ingredients

- 2 medium russet potatoes, cut into ½-inch cubes
- 2 tablespoons olive oil, divided
- ½ teaspoon sea salt, divided
- ½ teaspoon black pepper, divided
- 2 cups bite-size broccoli florets
- 4 cups shredded purple cabbage
- 1 tablespoon tamari
- 2 cups cooked brown rice

- Unhidden Valley Ranch Dressing or store-bought vegan ranch dressing
- ¼ cup pumpkin seeds
- ¼ cup thinly sliced scallions

Preparations

1. Preheat the oven to 425°F. Line a baking sheet with parchment paper.
2. In a large bowl, toss the potato cubes with 1 tablespoon of olive oil, ¼ teaspoon of salt, and ¼ teaspoon of pepper. Spread out on the prepared baking sheet. Bake for 15 minutes.
3. While the potatoes are baking, in the same bowl, toss the broccoli and cabbage with the tamari and the remaining 1 tablespoon of olive oil, ¼ teaspoon of salt, and ¼ teaspoon of pepper.
4. After the potatoes have baked for 15 minutes, toss them on the baking sheet with a spatula. Add the broccoli and cabbage on top of the potatoes and bake for 10 more minutes, or until the potatoes are fork-tender. Toss the vegetables and potatoes together until well combined.

5. Divide the rice among 4 bowls and top with the vegetable mixture. Drizzle with ranch dressing and sprinkle with the pumpkin seeds and scallions.

VARIATIONS

CABBAGE PATCH TACOS: Fill taco shells with the vegetable mixture and top with vegan cheddar shreds, salsa, and Sour Cream. Chop the broccoli into tiny bits when prepping the ingredients to ensure everything fits nicely inside the taco shells.

CABBAGE PATCH CHOPPY SALAD: Prepare all the ingredients as per the recipe, and toss with 1 head of romaine lettuce, chopped, and 1 chopped red bell pepper. When everything is combined, chop again for a super-delicious and colorful chopped salad. Top with ranch.

TIP: It is helpful to make a batch of rice or quinoa on a Sunday night so you have it to use throughout the week. It allows you to play around with vegetables and greens a bit, having a cooked grain on hand to add to the mix.

SAUCES, SOUPS, AND DIPS

55- Spicy Peanut Sauce

MAKES ½ CUP [2 TABLESPOONS = 1 SERVING]
PREP TIME: 5 minutes

This peanut sauce is perfect on rice noodles and stir-fried vegetables or served with fresh spring rolls. It's easy to whip up ahead of time, so I like to make a double batch and store it in a mason jar.

Ingredients

- ¼ cup honey
- 2 tablespoons creamy peanut butter
- ¼ cup low-sodium soy sauce
- ½ teaspoon red curry paste

Preparations

1. In a large bowl, whisk together the honey, peanut butter, soy sauce, and curry paste.
2. Store in an airtight container in the refrigerator for up to 1 week.

Substitution tip: Red curry paste can be found in the Asian section of most grocery stores. If you can't find it, feel free to substitute ½ teaspoon sriracha or another hot sauce.
GLUTEN-FREE: Use gluten-free tamari instead of soy sauce.
VEGAN: Use agave nectar instead of honey.

Per 2-tablespoon serving:
Calories: 59; Fat: 2g; Carbs: 10g; Fiber: 0g; Sugar: 10g; Protein: 2g; Sodium: 475mg

56- Enchilada Sauce

MAKES 2 CUPS [¼ CUP = 1 SERVING]
EQUIPMENT: Small saucepan
PREP TIME: 10 minutes
COOK TIME: 5 minutes

I could practically eat this Enchilada Sauce with a spoon. I came up with this recipe when I was craving enchiladas and wanted to avoid running to the store to buy a jar of sauce. It turned out to be so easy and I loved the flavor, so now I make this regularly.

Ingredients

- 2 tablespoons olive oil
- 2 tablespoons whole-wheat flour
- 2 tablespoons chili powder
- 2 cups low-sodium vegetable broth
- 2½ tablespoons tomato paste
- ¼ teaspoon cayenne pepper
- 1 teaspoon ground cumin
- Salt

Preparation

1. In a small saucepan, stir together the olive oil, flour, and chili powder. Cook over medium heat for 2 to 3 minutes until the mixture begins to bubble.
2. Whisk in the vegetable broth, tomato paste, cayenne pepper, and cumin.
3. Let the sauce simmer for 1 minute until it starts to thicken.
4. Remove from the heat and season with salt to taste.

Make-ahead tip: This Enchilada Sauce can be made up to 1 week in advance. Just store it in the refrigerator in an airtight container until you're ready to use it.

GLUTEN-FREE: Substitute any gluten-free flour.

Per ¼-cup serving: Calories: 58; Fat: 4g; Carbs: 4g; Fiber: 1g; Sugar: 1g; Protein: 2g; Sodium: 362mg

57- Tofu and mushroom soup

Total Time: 25 minutes | Servings: 4

Ingredients:

- 2 tbsp olive oil
- 1 garlic clove, minced
- 1 large yellow onion, finely chopped
- 1 tsp freshly grated ginger
- 1 cup vegetable stock
- 2 small potatoes, peeled and chopped
- ¼ tsp salt
- ¼ tsp black pepper
- 2 (14 oz) silken tofu, drained and rinsed
- 2/3 cup baby Bella mushrooms, sliced
- 1 tbsp chopped fresh oregano
- 2 tbsp chopped fresh parsley to garnish

Direction

Heat the olive oil in a medium pot over medium heat and sauté the garlic, onion, and ginger until soft and fragrant.

Pour in the vegetable stock, potatoes, salt, and black pepper. Cook until the potatoes soften, 12 minutes. Stir in the tofu and using an immersion blender, puree the ingredients until smooth. Mix in the mushrooms and simmer with the pot covered until the mushrooms warm up while occasionally stirring to ensure that the tofu doesn't curdle for 7 minutes. Stir oregano, and dish the soup. Garnish with the parsley and serve warm.

Nutritional values per serving: Calories – 156, Fat – 3 g, Carbohydrate – 23 g, Fiber –16 g, Protein – 17g

58- Avocado green soup

Total Time: 10 minutes | Servings: 4

Ingredients:

- 2 tbsp olive oil
- 1 ½ cup fresh kale, chopped coarsely
- 1 ½ cup fresh spinach, chopped coarsely
- 3 large avocados, halved, pitted and pulp extracted
- 2 cups of soy milk
- 2 cups no-sodium vegetable broth
- 3 tbsp chopped fresh mint leaves
- ¼ tsp salt
- ¼ tsp black pepper
- 2 limes, juiced

Direction

1. Heat the olive oil in a medium saucepan over medium heat and mix in the kale and spinach. Cook until wilted, 3 minutes, and turn off the heat.
2. Add the remaining ingredients and using an immersion blender, puree the soup until smooth.
3. Dish the soup and serve immediately.

Nutritional values per serving:

Calories – 100, Fat – 5 g, Carbohydrate – 13 g, Fiber –26 g, Protein – 14g

59- Spicy Black Bean Soup

Total Time: 15 minutes

Number of servings: 4

Ingredients:

•1 large onion, finely chopped

•2 tablespoons olive oil

•2 jalapeño peppers, deseeded, minced

•2 red bell peppers, chopped

•2 cups vegetable broth

•3 teaspoons freshly ground cumin

•2 tablespoons balsamic vinegar

•1 Hungarian pepper, deseeded, minced

- 4 cloves garlic, minced
- 2 cans (15 ounces each) black beans
- 1 avocado, peeled, pitted, chopped
- Salt to taste
- Pepper to taste
- 2 tablespoons fresh cilantro, chopped
- 4 tortillas

Directions:

1. Mash about 1 can of black beans. Add garlic to it and stir. Set aside.
2. Place a heavy-bottomed pot over medium heat. Add oil. When the oil is heated, add onions, peppers (all the varieties), and cumin and sauté until the vegetables are soft.
3. Add the rest of the ingredients except cilantro and bring to a boil.
4. Ladle into soup bowls and serve hot garnished with cilantro.

Nutritional values per serving:

Calories – 536, Fat – 22 g, Carbohydrate – 65 g, Fiber – 20 g, Protein – 21 g

60- Red Curry Quinoa Soup

Total Time: 30 minutes
Number of servings: 3
Ingredients:

- ½ tablespoon olive oil
- 1 small green bell pepper, deseeded, chopped
- 1 medium yellow onion, chopped
- 1 small sweet potato, chopped (about ¾ cup)
- ½ tablespoon red curry paste
- ½ cup quinoa
- 1 tablespoon lime juice
- A handful of fresh cilantro, chopped
- 1 clove garlic, chopped

- 1 teaspoon fresh ginger, peeled, chopped
- 2 cups vegetable broth or water
- Salt to taste

Directions:

1. Place a pot over medium-high heat. Add oil. When the oil is heated, add onion, sweet potato, and bell pepper.
2. Sauté for about 10 minutes.
3. Stir in ginger, garlic, and curry paste. Sauté until aromatic.
4. Add quinoa and stir-fry for a minute.
5. Add broth and stir.
6. When it begins to boil, lower the heat and cook until sweet potatoes and quinoa are cooked.
7. Turn off the heat. Stir in lime juice and salt.
8. Ladle into soup bowls. Sprinkle cilantro on top and serve.

Nutritional values per serving:

Calories – 164, Fat – 4 g, Carbohydrate – 26 g, Fiber – NA, Protein – 6 g

61- Split Pea Soup

Total Time: 20 minutes
Number of servings: 3
Ingredients:

- ½ tablespoon canola oil
- 1 medium white onion, finely chopped
- 1 small stalk celery, sliced
- 2 cups vegetable broth
- ¾ cups green split peas, rinsed
- ½ small russet potato, cubed
- ½ teaspoon ground cumin
- Freshly ground pepper to taste
- 1 cup water
- Salt to taste
- 1 small carrot, chopped

Directions
1. Place a soup pot over medium heat. Add oil. When the oil is heated, add onion, garlic, celery, and carrots and sauté for 3-4 minutes.
2. Add the rest of the ingredients to a large pot and stir.
3. Cook until the split peas and potatoes are tender. Add more water if required.

4. Mix well. Ladle into soup bowls and serve hot.

Nutritional values per serving:

Calories – 163, Fat – 3 g, Carbohydrate – 29 g, Fiber – 5 g, Protein – 7 g

62- Tofu Noodle Soup

e

Total Time: 15 minutes
Number of servings: 8

Ingredients:

- 1 large head of broccoli, cut into florets
- 2 blocks (14 ounces each) firm tofu, drained, pressed of excess moisture
- 2 teaspoons coconut oil
- 3 tablespoons olive oil
- 2 cups diced celery
- 2 cups chopped carrots
- 2 large onions, thinly sliced
- ¼ teaspoon black pepper
- ¼ teaspoon white pepper
- 4 tablespoons soy sauce

- 3 tablespoons rice vinegar (optional)
- 1 teaspoon red chili flakes
- 2 tablespoons nutritional yeast
- Salt to taste
- 16 ounces brown rice elbow pasta

Directions:

1. Spread the tofu cubes on a lined baking sheet.
2. Bake in a preheated oven at 400° F until light brown.
3. Place a large pot over medium-high heat. Add coconut oil and olive oil. When it is heated, add celery, onion, and carrot and sauté for about 4-5 minutes.
4. Add garlic, and all the spices. Sauté for a few seconds until aromatic.
5. Add tofu, pasta, and broccoli and stir-fry for a couple of minutes.
6. Add the rest of the ingredients and cook pasta until is al dente.
7. Ladle into soup bowls and serve.

Nutritional values per serving:

Calories – 404; Fat – 13 g,
Carbohydrate – 55 g; Fiber – 5 g,
Protein – 17 g

63- Hot and Sour Soup

Total Time: 15 minutes
Number of servings: 8
Ingredients:

- 8 cloves garlic, minced
- 4 tablespoons grated ginger, divided
- 2 packages (10 ounces each) mushrooms, sliced
- 16 fresh shiitake mushrooms, sliced
- 2 cans (8 ounces each) bamboo shoots, drained, julienned
- 2 packages (15 ounces each) firm or silken tofu, chopped into small cubes
- 3 cups frozen peas
- 8 cups water
- 4 tablespoons vegan chicken-flavored bouillon
- 2 teaspoons chili paste
- 4 tablespoons soy sauce or tamari
- 4 tablespoons rice wine vinegar
- 2 teaspoons sesame oil + extra to drizzle

Directions:

1. Add all the ingredients except half the ginger and peas into a soup pot.
2. Place the pot over medium heat. When it begins to boil, lower the heat and cook until slightly tender. Stir occasionally.
3. Add peas and half the ginger and stir. Cook for a minute.
4. Cover and let it sit for 5 minutes. Taste and adjust the seasoning if required.
5. Ladle into soup bowls and serve.

Nutritional values per serving:

Calories – 208, Fat – 7.4 g,
Carbohydrate – 21.6 g, Fiber – 5.4 g,
Protein – 19.2 g

64- Spicy Sundried Tomato Soup with White Beans & Swiss Chard

Total Time: 20 minutes
Number of servings: 4

Ingredients:

- 1 tablespoon olive oil
- ¼ teaspoon red pepper flakes
- 1 medium carrot, sliced
- ½ small zucchini, sliced
- ¾ cup chopped onion
- 1 stalk celery, chopped
- 1 teaspoon minced fresh rosemary
- 1 can (15 ounces) diced tomatoes

- ¼ cup oil-packed sundried tomatoes, drained, chopped
- 1 tablespoon oil from oil-packed sun-drained tomatoes
- ¼ teaspoon chopped thyme
- 2 cloves garlic, minced
- 1 cup vegetable broth
- ½ can (from 15 ounces can) white beans or cannellini beans, rinsed, drained
- 3 ounces Swiss chard, chopped
- ½ cup torn basil

Directions:

1. Place a soup pot over medium heat. Add oil. When the oil is heated, add garlic and red pepper flakes and sauté until aromatic.
2. Add onion, carrots, zucchini, celery, and rosemary and sauté until onions turn translucent.
3. Stir in the broth, beans, and ½ can tomatoes. Mix well. Add some of the mixtures into the blender. Add rest of the canned tomatoes, sundried tomatoes, and its oil and blend until smooth.
4. Pour it back into the pot.

5. Heat thoroughly. Add salt and pepper to taste. Let it simmer for a few minutes. Garnish with basil and serve.
6. Ladle into soup bowls.

Nutritional values per serving:

Calories – 169, Fat – 8 g, Carbohydrate – 21 g, Fiber – 6 g, Protein – 5 g

65- Lentil Spinach Soup

Total Time: 5 minutes
Number of servings: 8

Ingredients:

- 4 cups vegetable broth
- 1 teaspoon ground cumin
- Salt to taste
- Pepper to taste
- ½ cup water
- 6 tablespoons olive oil
- 2 whole carrots, peeled, chopped
- 2 tablespoons tomato paste
- ½ teaspoon smoked paprika
- ½ cup + 2 tablespoons dry lentils, green or brown or red, rinse
- 4 cups chopped spinach
- Juice of a lemon
- 1 medium onion, chopped

- 2-3 cloves garlic, minced
- 1 bay leaf

Directions:

1. Place a saucepan or soup pot over medium heat. Add oil. When the oil is heated, add onion and carrot and sauté until the onions are translucent.
2. Add garlic, paprika, cumin, and salt and sauté for a few seconds until fragrant.
3. Stir in the tomato paste and pepper and cook for a couple of minutes.
4. Add water, lentils, and broth and bring to a boil.
5. Lower the heat and cover with a lid. Simmer until the lentils are tender. Add more water or broth if required.
6. Add spinach and cook until spinach wilts. Turn off the heat. Add lemon juice and stir. Taste and add more seasonings or lemon juice if required.
7. Ladle into soup bowls and serve.

Nutritional values per serving:

Calories – 354, Fat – 12 g,
Carbohydrate – 41 g,
Fiber – 18 g, Protein – 21 g

66- Potato, Bean and Kale Soup

Total Time: 15 minutes
Number of servings: 3
Ingredients:

- 1 cup chopped onion
- 4 cups vegetable broth
- 1 can (15 ounces) pinto beans, drained or 1 ½ cups cooked pinto beans
- 3 cloves garlic, minced
- ½ pound small potatoes, chopped into bite-sized pieces
- 5 -6 cups chopped kale leaves, discard hard stems and ribs
- ½ teaspoon dried basil
- ½ teaspoon dried oregano
- ¼ teaspoon dried rosemary, crushed
- ¼ teaspoons red pepper flakes
- ¼ teaspoon fennel seeds
- ¼ cup nondairy milk of your choice (optional)
- 1 tablespoon nutritional yeast
- Salt to taste
- Pepper to taste

Directions:

1. Add all the ingredients except kale, milk, and nutritional yeast into a soup pot.
2. Place the pot over medium heat. Cover and cook until potatoes are tender.
3. Add kale and stir. Cover and cook for 5-8 minutes until kale is bright green in color and tender as well.
4. Add milk and nutritional yeast. Mix well.
5. Taste and adjust the seasoning if necessary.
6. Ladle into soup bowls and serve.

Nutritional values per serving:

Calories – 207, Fat – 1.3 g, Carbohydrate – 39.9 g, Fiber – 8.5 g, Protein – 11.1 g

67- Ethiopian Cabbage, Carrot, and Potato Stew

SERVES 4 TO 6 • PREP TIME: 10 MINUTES • COOK TIME: 20 MINUTES

Properly known as atakilt wat, this incredibly tasty stew is surprisingly simple to make. I have not had the opportunity to enjoy Ethiopian food as much as I would like, but I can say that each time has been a delightful experience. It's fun to sit around a plate with friends and share a meal, too! Some of my favorite Ethiopian restaurants I have found on my travels are Bunna Cafe (Brooklyn, New York), Blue Nile Cafe (Kansas City, Missouri), and Blue Nile Ethiopian Kitchen (Memphis, Tennessee). I hope you can check them out if you ever find yourself in those parts.

Ingredients:

- 3 russet potatoes, peeled and cut into ½-inch cubes
- 2 tablespoons olive oil
- 6 carrots, peeled, halved lengthwise, and cut into ½-inch slices
- 1 onion, chopped

- 4 garlic cloves, minced
- 1 tablespoon ground turmeric
- 1 teaspoon ground cumin
- 1 teaspoon ground ginger
- 1½ teaspoons sea salt
- 1½ cups low-sodium vegetable broth, divided
- 4 cups shredded or thinly sliced green cabbage

Preparation

1. Bring a large pot of water to a boil over medium-high heat. Add the potatoes and cook for 10 minutes, or until fork-tender. Drain and set aside.
2. While the potatoes are cooking, heat the oil in a large skillet over medium-high heat. Add the carrots and onion and sauté for 5 minutes. Add the garlic, turmeric, cumin, ginger, and salt and sauté for 1 additional minute, until fragrant.
3. Add the cooked potatoes and 1 cup of broth to the skillet, bring to a boil and reduce to a simmer. Scatter the cabbage on top of the potatoes. Cover and simmer for 3 minutes.

4. Mix the cabbage into the potatoes, add the remaining ½ cup of broth, cover, and simmer for 5 more minutes, or until the cabbage is wilted and tender. Stir the cabbage from time to time while cooking to incorporate it with the other ingredients as it continues to wilt.

VARIATIONS

ETHIOPIAN PITA: Serve this inside a pita with chopped spinach and brown rice. Drizzle with sriracha, if desired.

GREEN STEW: Use 2 cups of cabbage instead of 4 cups. After the cabbage has mostly wilted down, add 2 cups roughly chopped kale and simmer for 2 to 4 more minutes to allow the kale to wilt down. Stir into the stew until well incorporated.

TIP: Make this on a Sunday night for a bunch of mix-and-match meals throughout the week. It pairs nicely with almost any green or grain for a complete meal.

68- Creamy Butternut Squash Soup

SERVES 4 TO 6 • PREP TIME: 10 MINUTES • COOK TIME: 20 MINUTES

No need for heavy cream to achieve a decadent and rich texture in your soup—just let the veggies and a blender handle the task. Soup has always been helpful when I'm trying to maintain my weight, but the canned ones are full of sodium. Keep this recipe on hand for a quick, guilt-free, and satisfying lunch or dinner.

Ingredients:

- 1 butternut squash (roughly 2 pounds), peeled, seeded, and cut into ½-inch cubes
- 1 red bell pepper, seeded and chopped
- 1 large onion, chopped
- 3 garlic cloves, minced
- 4 cups low-sodium vegetable broth
- Juice of ½ lemon
- 2 tablespoons maple syrup
- ¾ teaspoon salt
- ¾ teaspoon black pepper

Preparation:

1. In a large stockpot, combine the squash, bell pepper, onion, garlic, and broth. Mix well to combine, cover, and bring to a boil. Reduce to a simmer and cook, covered, for 15 minutes, or until the squash is fork-tender. Add the lemon juice, maple syrup, salt, and pepper and stir well to combine.
2. Carefully transfer the soup to a blender. Remove the plug from the blender lid to allow steam to escape, hold a towel firmly over the hole in the lid, and blend until smooth. Start at the lowest speed possible and increase gradually until the soup is completely smooth. Depending on your blender capacity, this might have to be done in two batches. (If you have an immersion blender, it would work great here.)
3. Gently reheat over low heat to serve.

VARIATIONS

BUTTERNUT PASTA FAGIOLI: After the soup is completely blended and creamy, return it to the stockpot and add 1 (14-ounce) can diced tomatoes with their juice; 1 (14-ounce) can cannellini beans, rinsed and drained; and ½ pound elbow macaroni or small shells, cooked. Stir well to combine and let sit for 3 minutes to warm through.

BUTTERNUT SQUASH WITH ITALIAN SAUSAGE AND CORN: After the soup is completely blended and creamy, return it to the stockpot. In a medium skillet, heat 1 tablespoon olive oil over medium heat. Add 1 cup corn kernels and sauté for 4 to 6 minutes, until they're starting to brown. Add 2 vegan Italian sausages, cut into ¼-inch-thick slices, and sauté for an additional 2 to 4 minutes, until crispy. Mix the sausage and corn into the soup until well combined.

TIP: Make this ahead and heat as needed throughout the week. It will keep for up to a week in the refrigerator or up to a month in the freezer.

69- Basic BBQ Sauce

MAKES 2 CUPS • PREP TIME: 2 MINUTES • COOK TIME: 5 MINUTES • STORAGE: 2 WEEKS IN THE REFRIGERATOR

My partner has a dipping-sauce infatuation. He will often order food at a restaurant not because he wants the actual food; he's after the variety of dipping sauces that come with the food. When faced with a choice, barbecue sauce is always his first request. I created this one to make sure I could throw something together for him when we don't have any store-bought barbecue on hand.

Ingredients:

- 1 cup ketchup
- 1 tablespoon plus 1 teaspoon red wine vinegar
- 2 tablespoons dark-brown sugar
- 2 teaspoons paprika
- ½ teaspoon black pepper
- ¼ teaspoon sea salt

Preparation:

1. In a small saucepot, whisk together all the ingredients and bring to a simmer over medium heat. Cook for 3 minutes, or until the sugar has dissolved completely. Enjoy warm or chilled

VARIATIONS

HONEY-FREE SWEET BBQ SAUCE: Add 2 tablespoons agave or maple syrup and cook as directed.

BOURBON BBQ SAUCE: In a medium skillet, heat 1 tablespoon olive oil over medium heat. Add ½ cup chopped onion and sauté for 3 minutes, or until soft. Add ½ cup bourbon and cook it down until the liquid has reduced and the onion is still wet but the skillet has no more watery liquid, about 5 minutes. Add the ingredients as listed for Basic BBQ Sauce and cook as directed.

TIP: You can adjust the sugar and paprika to reach the sweetness and heat you desire.

SMOOTHIES AND BEVERAGES

70- Green Tea Smoothie

SERVES 1
EQUIPMENT: Blender
PREP TIME: 5 minutes

I love this smoothie during the warm summer months because it's so light and refreshing. The green tea adds flavor without adding sugar. For a twist, substitute frozen mango for the frozen peaches.

Ingredients:

- 3 large ice cubes
- ¾ cup frozen peach chunks
- ⅓ cup green tea cooled
- ¼ cup plain Greek yogurt
- 1 teaspoon honey

Preparation:

1. Add the ice cubes, peaches, green tea, yogurt, and honey to a blender and blend until smooth.
2. Pour into a large glass and drink right away.

Ingredient tip: Green tea contains caffeine, so this is a great smoothie to perk you up in the morning.

DAIRY-FREE: Use coconut milk yogurt or almond milk yogurt instead of Greek yogurt.

VEGAN: Go dairy-free, and substitute maple syrup or agave nectar for the honey.

Per serving: Calories: 106; Fat: 1g; Carbs: 19g; Fiber: 2g; Sugar: 17g; Protein: 7g; Sodium: 25mg

71-Coconut-Mango Smoothie

SERVES 2
EQUIPMENT: Blender
PREP TIME: 5 minutes

This is one of my all-time favorite smoothie combinations. It tastes like my favorite frozen yogurt, but since the mango and pineapple are already sweet, it doesn't require any additional sweetener.

Ingredients:

- 1 cup ice cubes
- 1 cup frozen mango chunks
- 1 cup frozen pineapple chunks
- 1 cup unsweetened coconut milk or almond milk
- 2 tablespoons unsweetened coconut flakes
- 1 tablespoon chia seeds (optional)

Preparation:

1. Blend the ice, mango, pineapple, and coconut milk or almond milk in a blender until smooth.

2. Divide between two glasses and sprinkle with the coconut flakes and chia seeds (if using).

Ingredient tip: Chia seeds contain lots of fiber and healthy fats, which can help balance blood sugar. They are a great addition to smoothies like this one, which contains natural sugars from the fruit. You can find them at many supermarkets and health food stores.

Per serving: Calories:

Fat: 10g; Carbs: 41g; Fiber: 5g; Sugar: 36g; Protein: 2g; Sodium: 88mg

72- Blueberry Lemonade Smoothie

SERVES 1 • PREP TIME: 5 MINUTES

My life drastically changed when I started sneaking greens into my morning smoothie. I could actually feel the difference in my body from getting nutrients that were broken down into the most digestible form.
Honestly, I love smoothies so much, I suck them down like a milkshake. With smoothies like these, I don't have to feel bad about that!

Ingredients:

- 1 cup roughly chopped kale
- 3/4 cup frozen blueberries
- 1 cup unsweetened soy or almond milk
- Juice of 1 lemon
- 1 tablespoon maple syrup

Preparation:

Combine all the ingredients in a blender and blend until smooth. Enjoy immediately.

VARIATIONS

STRAWBERRY LEMONADE SMOOTHIE: Replace the blueberries with 1 cup strawberries.

TROPICAL SMOOTHIE: Replace the blueberries with ½ cup mango chunks and ½ cup pineapple chunks.

TIP: The amount of liquid depends on your blender and its speed, so you may need to use more milk. If you want to cut caloric content, use half milk and half water, or just water.

73- Mango Key Lime Pie Smoothie

SERVES 1 • PREP TIME: 5 MINUTES

We are gathered here today to witness the union of mangos and limes. If anyone has any objections, kindly keep your mouth shut. This drink is velvety smooth, with the perfect amount of tart and sweet, and who doesn't love pie for breakfast? This is the pie you can feel good about.

Ingredients:

- ¼ avocado
- 1 cup baby spinach
- ½ cup frozen mango chunks
- 1 cup unsweetened soy or almond milk
- Juice of 1 lime (preferably a Key lime, if you can find one!)
- 1 tablespoon maple syrup

Preparation:

Combine all the ingredients in a blender and blend until smooth. Enjoy immediately.

VARIATIONS

MANGO KEY LIME PIE SMOOTHIE BOWL: Pour the smoothie into a cereal bowl. Top with granola, shredded coconut, and goji berries for a filling and healthful start to your morning.

LEMON-LIME SMOOTHIE: Replace the mango with 1 frozen banana and use the juice of both 1 lemon and 1 lime.

TIP: Use frozen fruit in smoothies to avoid having to add ice to make your smoothie thick and cold. Ice can water a smoothie down, resulting in a weaker flavor.

74- Banana Cream Pie Smoothie

SERVES 1 • PREP TIME: 5 MINUTES

I don't put greens in all my smoothies; sometimes I make them because I want something that tastes truly sinful. This decadent and creamy smoothie satisfies my sweet tooth every time. While this isn't a green smoothie, it's certainly a heck of a lot better for me than a slice of pie or a doughnut, and I still feel like I'm treating myself!

Ingredients:

- 1 banana, frozen
- 1 cup unsweetened soy or almond milk
- ¼ cup uncooked rolled oats
- 1 tablespoon maple syrup
- Pinch ground cinnamon
- Pinch sea salt

Preparation:
Combine all the ingredients in a blender and blend until smooth. Serve immediately.

VARIATIONS

BOSTON CREAM PIE: Add 1 tablespoon fair-trade unsweetened cocoa powder.

VELVET PEANUT BUTTER CHOCOLATE PIE: Add 1 tablespoon fair-trade unsweetened cocoa powder and 2 tablespoons creamy peanut butter.

TIP: Oats have a slight natural sweetness; if you are cutting back on calories, this recipe is still delicious without the maple syrup.

75- Berry Beetsicle Smoothie

SERVES 1 • PREP TIME: 3 MINUTES

Unicorns are all the rage these days. If you feel so inclined, you can skip right to the unicorn variation on this smoothie with a dollop of Coconut Whipped Cream and some rainbow sprinkles. It has that beautiful pink color required of all things unicorn. This recipe is quick, healthful, and so beautiful that I feel like Wonder Woman when I drink it!

Ingredients:

- ½ cup peeled and diced beets
- ½ cup frozen raspberries
- 1 frozen banana
- 1 tablespoon maple syrup
- 1 cup unsweetened soy or almond milk

Preparation:
Combine all the ingredients in a blender and blend until smooth.

VARIATIONS

UNICORN SMOOTHIE: Make this smoothie and set it aside in the refrigerator. Rinse out the blender and combine 1 more frozen banana with ½ cup unsweetened soy or almond milk and 2 blueberries (yes, just 2). Blend until smooth; it should be blue. Pour half of the Berry Beetsicle Smoothie into a drinking glass or mason jar, then the blueberry mixture, then the rest of the beetsicle. Top with Coconut Whipped Cream and vegan rainbow sprinkles.
CITRUS-BEET SMOOTHIE: Omit the milk and raspberries. Add ½ cup peeled and chopped orange and 1 cup orange juice.
TIP: There's no way of getting around it, beets are a beautiful red-producing machine, and this means on your hands. It's worth it to invest in a box of rubber gloves from the dollar store when you are starting a love affair with beets!

76- Fruit Skewers with Dark Chocolate Yogurt Dip

SERVES 4
EQUIPMENT: Bamboo skewers
PREP TIME: 15 minutes

Warning: You might end up eating this chocolate yogurt dip with a spoon! But don't worry, it's full of good-for-you ingredients. I like to use dark cocoa powder, which you can find at most grocery stores. Not only does it give this a rich, chocolaty taste, cocoa is also a good source of iron.

Ingredients:

For the dip

- ½ cup plain Greek yogurt
- 2 tablespoons dark cocoa powder
- ¼ teaspoon pure
- vanilla extract
- 1 tablespoon honey

For the fruit skewers

- 1 cup strawberries, hulled and halved
- 1 cup peeled, cored, and chopped pineapple (about ¼ medium pineapple)

- 1 cup pitted and chopped peaches (1 to 2 peaches)
- 1 cup blackberries

Preparation:

TO MAKE THE DIP

Combine the yogurt, cocoa powder, vanilla, and honey. You can simply stir them together in a medium bowl, or, if your cocoa powder is clumpy, you may want to blend the ingredients in a blender for a smoother texture.

TO MAKE THE SKEWERS

1. Thread the chunks of fruit onto bamboo skewers, alternating types of fruit for variety. There should be 6 to 8 pieces of fruit on each skewer.
2. Serve the skewers with a side of the dip to dunk the pieces of fruit in.

Make-ahead tip: The dip can be made up to 2 days in advance and stored in the refrigerator in an airtight container. But cut the fruit and assemble the skewers just before serving.

DAIRY-FREE: Use coconut milk yogurt or almond milk yogurt in place of the Greek yogurt. If your non-dairy yogurt has added sugar, taste the dip before adding the honey; you may not need as much.

VEGAN: Go dairy-free, and also replace the honey with agave nectar.

Per serving: Calories: 99; Fat: 1g; Carbs: 20g; Fiber: 5g; Sugar: 14g; Protein: 5g; Sodium: 14mg

77- *Salt-and-Vinegar Brussels Sprout Chips*

SERVES 4
EQUIPMENT: Nonstick baking sheet
PREP TIME: 15 minutes
COOK TIME: 20 minutes

Brussels sprout chips might sound weird, but you'll be surprised at how good they are. When the thin leaves of a Brussels sprout are baked, they get super crispy. You want the oven temperature to be low because the goal is not to roast the sprout leaves but to dehydrate them, which makes them crunchy without needing a lot of oil. The white balsamic vinegar gives these a flavor that will remind you of your favorite salt-and-vinegar potato chips.

Ingredients:

- 1 pound Brussels sprouts
- 1 tablespoon avocado oil
- 2 tablespoons white balsamic vinegar
- ¼ teaspoon salt

Preparation:

1. Preheat the oven to 250°F.
2. Trim the ends off the Brussels sprouts and peel the layers apart into individual leaves.
3. Combine the avocado oil and vinegar in a large zip-top bag. Add the sprout leaves to the bag and gently toss until evenly coated.
4. Spread the leaves in a single layer on a nonstick baking sheet and bake for 15 to 20 minutes until they're brown and crispy.
5. Sprinkle with salt.

Prep tip: Peeling apart Brussels sprouts might sound time-consuming, but the larger layers will typically fall off after you trim the ends. Separate the rest of the larger leaves, and when you get to the tightly compacted center, set it aside. Save the small hearts to toss into a salad or stir-fry.

Per serving: Calories: 81; Fat: 4g; Carbs: 10g; Fiber: 4g; Sugar: 3g; Protein: 4g; Sodium: 176mg

78- Peanut Butter Granola Bars

MAKES 8 BARS [1 BAR = 1 SERVING]
EQUIPMENT: 9-by-4-inch nonstick loaf pan
PREP TIME: 5 minutes
COOK TIME: 15 minutes

These granola bars are a perfectly portable snack that you can make at the start of the week and grab on your way out the door. If you don't have almond flour, you can grind almonds in a blender or food processor to make your own.

Ingredients:

- Nonstick cooking spray
- ⅓ cup honey
- ½ cup natural crunchy peanut butter
- ½ cup rolled oats
- ½ cup almond flour
- ½ cup sliced almonds

Preparation:

1. Preheat the oven to 350°F. Spray a 9-by-4-inch nonstick loaf pan with nonstick cooking spray.

2. In a large bowl, combine the honey and peanut butter.
3. Stir in the oats, almond flour, and almonds until combined.
4. Press the oat mixture into the bottom of the prepared loaf plan.
5. Bake for 14 to 17 minutes until the edges just begin to brown. It might still be a little soft but will firm up when cool.
6. Make sure to let cool completely in the pan, then cut into 8 bars.
7. Store in an airtight container.

Substitution tip: You can substitute cashew butter or almond butter for the peanut butter if you like.

VEGAN: Use agave nectar instead of honey.

Per bar: Calories: 298; Fat: 20g; Carbs: 25g; Fiber: 4g; Sugar: 15g; Protein: 9g; Sodium: 67mg

79- Garlic Sweet Potato Oven Fries

SERVES 4
EQUIPMENT: Nonstick baking sheet
PREP TIME: 10 minutes
COOK TIME: 20 minutes

Veggie burgers served with a side of sweet potato fries are a common dish at our house, especially in the summertime. The only things I love more than crispy sweet potato fries are crispy sweet potato fries topped with garlic. Make sure you roast the sweet potato wedges long enough that they get browned on the outside.

Ingredients:

- Nonstick cooking spray
- 2 large sweet potatoes
- 1 tablespoon olive oil
- 4 garlic cloves, minced
- 1 teaspoon salt

Preparation:

1. Preheat the oven to 450°F. Spray a nonstick baking sheet with nonstick cooking spray.

2. Peel the sweet potatoes and cut them into wedges.
3. In a large bowl, toss the potato wedges with the olive oil. Spread them evenly on the prepared baking sheet.
4. Roast for 10 minutes, flip and continue to roast for 10 minutes more or until browned on both sides.
5. Sprinkle with garlic and salt before serving.

Prep tip: As much as possible, cut the sweet potatoes into uniform wedges. That will ensure that you're able to get them nicely browned without burning any or leaving some undercooked.

Per serving: Calories: 101; Fat: 4g; Carbs: 12g; Fiber: 2g; Sugar: 4g; Protein: 1g; Sodium: 604mg

80- White Bean and Sage Dip

MAKES 2 CUPS [1/4 CUP = 1 SERVING]
EQUIPMENT: Medium nonstick skillet, blender, or food processor.
PREP TIME: 5 minutes
COOK TIME: 5 minutes

This dip might remind you of hummus, but cannellini beans are softer than chickpeas, so the texture is extra creamy. Cooking the sage and garlic in olive oil gives this dip its savory flavor, so don't skip that step. Serve this with vegetables or pita chips at your next party.

Ingredients:

- ¼ cup olive oil
- 1 teaspoon chopped fresh sage
- 3 garlic cloves, minced
- 2 (15-ounce) cans cannellini beans, drained and rinsed
- 1 tablespoon pine nuts (optional)
- Cucumbers and carrots, cut into sticks, or pita chips, for serving

Preparation:

1. Heat the olive oil in a medium nonstick skillet over medium heat for 1 minute. Add the sage and garlic and continue to cook for 2 minutes.
2. Remove from the heat and stir in the cannellini beans.
3. Scrape the mixture into a blender or food processor and blend until slightly chunky.
4.Sprinkle with the pine nuts (if using) just before serving.
5. Serve with cut cucumbers, carrots, and/or pita chips.

Per ¼-cup serving: Calories: 163; Fat: 7g; Carbs: 19g; Fiber: 7g; Sugar: 2g; Protein: 7g; Sodium: 379mg

81. BANANA-WALNUT OVERNIGHT OATS

PREP: 5 MINUTES (plus overnight soaking)
COOK: 0 MINUTES TOTAL: 5 MINUTES

My family loves overnight oats—they're hearty, delicious, and super easy to make. Plus, because they can be prepared the night before, they make starting the day on a healthy note a lot easier. You can easily make this recipe in larger batches to be enjoyed throughout the week.

Ingredients:

- 1 cup rolled oats
- 4 teaspoons chia seeds
- 1½ cups sweetened vanilla almond milk or other nondairy milk
- 1 large ripe banana, diced
- ¼ cup chopped raw walnuts
- 1 tablespoon pure maple syrup (optional)

Preparation:

In a small bowl, stir together the oats, chia seeds, and almond milk.

Refrigerate the mixture overnight, or for at least a few hours.

When ready to serve, stir the oats and pour them into a mason jar. Top with the banana and walnuts.

Drizzle the maple syrup over the top for an extra touch of natural sweetness, if desired.

82. *HERBED WHITE BEAN AND PEA SALAD*

PREP: 5 MINUTES COOK: 0 MINUTES TOTAL: 5 MINUTES

This salad is so delicious and easy to make. Keep it light and simple with a slice of multigrain toast or scoop it into romaine lettuce leaves. For a more filling meal, enjoy it with a side of cooked quinoa or brown rice. Make it your own.

Ingredients:

- 1 cup frozen peas
- 1 (15-ounce) can butter beans or cannellini beans, drained and rinsed
- ½ red bell pepper, minced
- 1 scallion, thinly sliced

DRESSING

- ½ cup minced fresh mint
- ½ cup minced fresh parsley leaves
- 1 tablespoon minced fresh dill
- 1 teaspoon minced garlic
- Juice of 1 lemon
- ¼ teaspoon sea salt

- 1 tablespoon extra-virgin olive oil

TO SERVE

- 1 avocado, sliced
- Freshly ground black pepper
- Fresh herbs (such as basil, thyme, and/or tarragon)

Preparation:

Put the frozen peas in a colander and set them under cool running water to thaw. Drain the peas well, then transfer them to a large bowl and add the beans, bell pepper, and scallion.

TO MAKE THE DRESSING In a medium bowl, whisk together all the dressing ingredients and 2 tablespoons of water. (Alternatively, combine the ingredients in a food processor and process until smooth.) Taste and adjust the seasoning, if necessary.

Pour the dressing over the pea mixture and stir to combine.

Top the salad with the sliced avocado. Season with a few grinds of black pepper and serve with your favorite fresh herbs sprinkled over the top.

83. RAW VEGGIE SALAD

PREP: 10 MINUTES COOK: 0 MINUTES
TOTAL: 10 MINUTES

We love raw veggies in our home, and we especially love how they make us feel after we've enjoyed them as a meal. Here's a family favorite you're bound to enjoy as much as we do. It's loaded with health-boosting nutrients, not to mention flavor.

Ingredients:

DRESSING

- ⅓ cup stone-ground mustard
- ¼ cup cider vinegar
- 1 teaspoon pure maple syrup
- ¼ teaspoon freshly ground black pepper
- 1 tablespoon fresh lemon juice

SALAD

- 1 large cucumber, spiralized
- 1 large carrot, spiralized
- 1 large broccoli stem, tough outer layer peeled, spiralized
- ¼ cup pitted kalamata olives
- 1 cup cherry tomatoes, halved

- ¼ cup pine nuts

Preparation:

TO MAKE THE DRESSING In a small bowl, whisk together all the dressing ingredients and 1 tablespoon water.

TO MAKE THE SALAD In a large bowl, combine the cucumber, carrot, and broccoli.

Pour the dressing over the veggies and toss to coat.

Top with the olives, tomatoes, and pine nuts and serve.

TIP: Feel free to add any other veggies you have handy. This recipe is a great way to use up fresh produce that's languishing in your fridge.

84. PEANUT BUTTER SMOOTHIE BOWL

PREP: 5 MINUTES COOK: 0 MINUTES
TOTAL: 5 MINUTES

Smoothie bowls are a fun way to start the day, especially when they're as delicious and nutritious as this one!

Ingredients:

- 1½ ripe bananas: 1 frozen, ½ sliced
- ½ cup almond milk or other nondairy milk
- 2 tablespoons peanut butter
- 2 tablespoons raw peanuts
- Fresh berries

Preparation:

In a blender, combine the frozen banana, almond milk, and peanut butter and blend until smooth.

Scoop the smoothie into a bowl and top with the sliced banana and peanuts. Garnish with fresh berries for a little extra color and an added antioxidant boost.

85. CHIA OAT PEANUT BUTTER PARFAIT

PREP: 5 MINUTES (plus overnight soaking)
COOK: 0 MINUTES TOTAL: 5 MINUTES

This parfait is a nutritious and easy make-ahead breakfast. The delicious combination of oats, chia, blackberries, and peanut butter is a great way to fuel your day!

Ingredients:

- 3 tablespoons chia seeds
- 2 cups unsweetened vanilla almond milk
- 1 teaspoon pure maple syrup
- ½ cup rolled oats
- 4 tablespoons peanut butter
- 4 tablespoons blackberries

Preparation:

In a mason jar or other glass container with a lid, stir together the chia seeds, 1 cup of almond milk, and maple syrup.

In a separate jar or another glass container with a lid, stir together the oats and the remaining 1 cup almond milk.

Cover both jars and refrigerate overnight.

When ready to enjoy, stir the oat and chia mixtures to make sure each mixture is well combined and to break apart any clumps. In a serving jar, layer half the oat mixture, 1 tablespoon of the peanut butter, and half the chia pudding. Top with 1 tablespoon more peanut butter and 2 tablespoons of the blackberries. Repeat the layers in a second jar using the remaining ingredients and serve.

86. BLUEBERRY BLISS BOWL

PREP: 5 MINUTES COOK: 0 MINUTES
TOTAL: 5 MINUTES

Smoothie bowls are a quick and easy way to enjoy a nutritious and delicious breakfast that provides the energy you'll need to get your day going. This one is loaded with antioxidant power!

Ingredients:

- 1½ ripe bananas: 1 frozen and ½ sliced
- 1 cup frozen blueberries
- 1 tablespoon ground chia seeds ½ cup almond milk or other nondairy milk
- ½ cup fresh blackberries

Preparation:

In a blender, combine the frozen banana, ½ cup of the blueberries, chia seeds, and almond milk, and blend until smooth.

Serve the smoothie in a bowl, topped with the remaining ½ cup blueberries, the blackberries, and the sliced banana.

TIP: Feel free to get creative with different fruit and seed toppings.

87. AVOCADO TOAST WITH SUNFLOWER SEEDS AND SPROUTS

PREP: 5 MINUTES COOK: 5 MINUTES TOTAL: 10 MINUTES

This is an all-time family favorite. I fix it most days of the week for my kids. Avocados are incredibly nutritious and contain a wide variety of vitamins and minerals—they even have more potassium than bananas. They're also loaded with fiber and contain heart-healthy monounsaturated fats. Avocado, however, isn't the only superstar in this recipe. The sunflower seeds and sprouts make this a perfect meal, any time of day.

Ingredients:

- 2 slices gluten-free vegan bread
- ½ Hass avocado
- Juice of ½ lime
- 1 tablespoon raw sunflower seeds
- ½ cup broccoli sprouts
- Dash of smoked paprika

Preparation:

Toast the bread.

In a small bowl, use a fork to mash the avocado with the lime juice.

Spread the mashed avocado over the toast. Top with the sunflower seeds, sprouts, and paprika and serve.

88. MEXICAN-INSPIRED BEAN SALAD

PREP: 10 MINUTES COOK: 0 MINUTES TOTAL: 10 MINUTES

This delicious salad is made with a nutritious combination of plant superstars, all mixed together in a citrus dressing and topped with sliced avocado. If your kids will be enjoying this salad and are sensitive to spicy foods, you can skip the chili powder. If not, for a more authentic Mexican experience, feel free to add minced jalapeños for an added kick, and use cilantro instead of parsley.

Ingredients:

- 1 (15-ounce) can black-eyed peas, drained and rinsed
- 1 (15-ounce) can pinto beans, drained and rinsed
- 1 (15-ounce) can of black beans, drained and rinsed
- 1 (15-ounce) can corn, drained and rinsed
- 1 cup cherry tomatoes, quartered
- ⅓ red onion, minced

- Leaves from ½ bunch parsley or cilantro, minced (about ¾ cup)
- Juice of 2 lemons
- 1 tablespoon olive oil (optional)
- 1 tablespoon red wine vinegar
- ½ teaspoon sea salt, plus more as needed
- ¼ teaspoon freshly ground black pepper, plus more as needed
- ¼ teaspoon chili powder, or to taste (optional)
- 1 avocado, sliced

Preparation:

In a large bowl, combine the black-eyed peas, pinto beans, black beans, and corn. Add the tomatoes, onion, parsley, lemon juice, olive oil (if using), vinegar, salt, pepper, and chili powder (if using). Mix together to combine. Taste and adjust the seasoning if necessary. Top with the avocado, season with salt and pepper and serve.

89. *CHICKPEA NO-TUNA SALAD SANDWICH*

PREP: 10 MINUTES COOK: 0 MINUTES TOTAL: 10 MINUTES

Introducing another family favorite: "no-tuna" salad made with chickpeas. We make this a couple of times a week and enjoy it in a sandwich, with sliced carrots and celery sticks, as a dip for gluten-free crackers, or in a generous scoop atop a green salad.

Ingredients:

- 1 (15-ounce) can chickpeas, drained and rinsed, loose skins discarded
- 2 tablespoons shredded carrot
- 2 tablespoons minced red onion
- 2 tablespoons minced fresh parsley, or 1 tablespoon dried
- 2 tablespoons vegan mayo
- 1 teaspoon Dijon mustard
- Pinch of garlic powder
- Juice of ½ lemon
- ⅛ teaspoon sea salt, or to taste
- Freshly ground black pepper

- Lettuce or other greens
- ½ tomato, sliced
- 4 slices gluten-free vegan bread

Preparation:

In a medium bowl, mash the chickpeas with a fork or the bottom of a cup until broken down to a creamy but still slightly chunky consistency. Add the carrot, onion, parsley, mayo, mustard, garlic powder, lemon juice, salt, and pepper to taste. Mix well to combine. Taste and adjust the seasoning if necessary.

Divide the lettuce, tomato, and no-tuna salad between 2 slices of the bread, then top each with a second slice of bread and serve.

TIP: Make a large batch of no-tuna salad to have on hand throughout the week and store it in an airtight container in the fridge for up to 5 days.

90. *BANANA-NUT QUINOA BOWL*

PREP: 5 MINUTES COOK: 5 MINUTES TOTAL: 10 MINUTES

I love keeping cooked quinoa in the refrigerator for easy lunch bowls. Here I use it for a delicious and hearty breakfast that is sure to warm your heart. Quinoa is a great source of complete protein. When combined with banana, blueberries, and walnuts, it makes a perfect breakfast for the entire family.

Ingredients:

- 2 cups cooked quinoa (recipe follows)
- ¾ cup unsweetened vanilla almond milk or other nondairy milk
- 1 banana, sliced
- ⅓ cup chopped raw walnuts
- ½ cup blueberries
- 1 tablespoon almond butter (optional)

Preparation:

In a small saucepan, combine the quinoa and almond milk and cook over medium heat until the quinoa has absorbed the liquid.

Pour the cooked quinoa into a small bowl and top with the banana, walnuts, and blueberries. Drizzle some almond butter over the top, if desired, and enjoy.

TIP: This is a very versatile dish and can be enjoyed with a variety of fruit (fresh or dried) and nut butter.

91. *HOMEMADE OAT MILK*

PREP: 5 MINUTES COOK: 0 MINUTES
TOTAL: 5 MINUTES

I love preparing my own dairy-alternative drinks at home. They're easy to make and less expensive than commercial varieties. What's more, making grain milk and nut milk at home lets you be in control of the ingredients that go into them. This oat milk recipe is nut-free and ready in 5 minutes or less. Plus, it's smooth and delicious, the perfect non-dairy milk.

Ingredients:

- 1 cup uncooked steel-cut oats
- 6 pitted dates, or more to taste
- ½ teaspoon pure vanilla extract

Preparation:

In a high-speed blender, combine the oats, dates, vanilla, and 4 cups of filtered water and blend at high speed until smooth.

Strain the oat milk through a nut milk bag or a fine-mesh sieve lined with cheesecloth into a large mason jar.

Store the oat milk in the refrigerator, covered, for 4 to 5 days. Separation is natural—just shake thoroughly to recombine before using. Enjoy it in smoothies or overnight oats and with granola.

92. *KALE BREAKFAST SALAD*

PREP: 10 MINUTES COOK: 0 MINUTES
TOTAL: 10 MINUTES

Kale for breakfast? You bet! There's no better way to break your fast in the morning than with a super green. Kale is a great source of fiber, protein, and vitamins A, B, C, and K. This easy-to-make salad is a sure way to add an energizing boost to your morning.

Ingredients:

DRESSING

- 1 tablespoon Dijon mustard
- Dash of freshly ground black pepper
- 2 tablespoons balsamic vinegar
- 1 tablespoon fresh lime juice
- 1½ teaspoons pure maple syrup

SALAD

- 1 small bunch kale, stemmed and chopped
- 1 large grapefruit, peeled and separated into sections
- 1 large orange, peeled and separated into sections

- ½ cup pomegranate arils
- ⅓ cup raw hulled pumpkin seeds

Preparation:

TO MAKE THE DRESSING In a small bowl, whisk together all the dressing ingredients until well blended.

TO MAKE THE SALAD Put the kale in a large bowl and pour over the dressing. Using clean hands, massage the dressing into the kale to soften the leaves.

Top the kale with the citrus sections, pomegranate arils, and pumpkin seeds.

TIP: Experiment with different fruits and seeds for dozens of other healthy topping options.

93. *HUMMUS*

PREP: 5 MINUTES COOK: 0 MINUTES
TOTAL: 5 MINUTES

Made from chickpeas, hummus is a must-have for plant-based eating. Use it on sandwiches, as a dip, or—my favorite—to spread on stuffed grape leaves.

Ingredients:

- 1 (15-ounce) can chickpeas, drained (¼ cup liquid from the can reserve), and rinsed
- 2 tablespoons tahini
- Juice of 1 lime
- ¼ teaspoon sea salt

Preparation:

In a high-speed blender or food processor, combine the chickpeas, tahini, lime juice, and salt. Blend until smooth, adding 1 tablespoon of the reserved chickpea can liquid at a time until the desired consistency is reached. Serve immediately or store in an airtight container in the refrigerator for up to 1 week.

94. *HEMP HEART FRUIT SALAD*

PREP: 5 MINUTES COOK: 0 MINUTES TOTAL: 5 MINUTES

Here's one of my favorite fruit salads. Hemp hearts are loaded with protein and heart-healthy omega-3 fatty acids. The berries are antioxidant champions. Together, they make a perfect meal that's as easy to make as it is delicious and filling.

Ingredients:

- 1 cup blueberries
- 1 cup blackberries
- 1 cup sliced strawberries
- 1 cup raspberries
- ¼ cup hemp hearts
- Juice of 1 orange

Preparation:

In a medium bowl, combine all the berries.

Add the hemp hearts and orange juice. Toss to coat evenly and serve.

TIP: Top the salad with your favorite coconut yogurt or almond yogurt for a little extra fuel.

95. BERRY CHIA PUDDING

PREP: 5 MINUTES (plus overnight soaking)
COOK: 0 MINUTES TOTAL: 5 MINUTES

Who doesn't love pudding? Here's a guilt-free take on the pudding that incorporates chia seeds, which are loaded with heart-healthy omega-3 fatty acids, vitamins, minerals, antioxidants, and fiber. Enjoy this dish as a dessert or for breakfast.

Ingredients:

- 2 cups almond milk or other nondairy milk
- ½ cup chia seeds
- 1 cup blueberries
- 1 cup raspberries
- 1 cup sliced strawberries

Preparation:

In a mason jar or other glass container with a lid, stir together the almond milk and chia seeds until well combined. Cover and refrigerate overnight.

When ready to serve, divide the pudding between two clean mason jars, alternating with layers of the berries.

96. *PEANUT BUTTER AND JELLY CHIA PUDDING*

PREP: 5 MINUTES (plus overnight soaking)
COOK: 0 MINUTES TOTAL: 5 MINUTES

This recipe turns the traditional PB&J sandwich into a tasty pudding that's guaranteed to become a classic on its own. Enjoy this pudding as a dessert or for breakfast.

Ingredients:

- 2 cups almond milk or other nondairy milk
- ½ cup chia seeds
- 1½ cups blueberries
- 1½ cups raspberries
- ¼ cup crunchy peanut butter
- 2 tablespoons raw peanuts

Preparation:

In a mason jar or other glass container with a lid, stir together the almond milk and chia seeds until well combined. Cover and refrigerate overnight.

Combine the berries in a bowl and lightly mash them with a fork.
When ready to serve, divide the pudding between two clean mason jars, alternating with layers of mashed berries and peanut butter.
Top with the peanuts and enjoy!

97. PINEAPPLE NICE CREAM

PREP: 10 MINUTES COOK: 0 MINUTES
TOTAL: 10 MINUTES

This is an incredibly creamy tropical treat. It is completely free of dairy and eggs but bursting with pineapple flavor.

Ingredients:

- 2 cups frozen pineapple chunks
- ½ teaspoon fresh lime juice

Preparation:

In a high-speed blender, combine the pineapple and lime juice. Blend on low, slowly increasing the speed to high, until smooth and creamy, about 30 seconds. Add water, 1 tablespoon at a time, if needed to facilitate blending.

Enjoy immediately or pour into an airtight container and freeze until ready to enjoy. It can be kept in the freezer for up to 1 month.

98. BANANA NICE CREAM BOWL WITH PECANS

PREP: 10 MINUTES COOK: 0 MINUTES
TOTAL: 10 MINUTES

You can easily whip up your own guilt-free ice cream using bananas as a creamy base. The pecans add an extra boost of protein, fiber, vitamins, and minerals.

Ingredients:

- 2 frozen large bananas
- ⅓ cup raw pecans
- ¼ cup pure maple syrup

Preparation:

In a food processor, pulse the frozen bananas until broken down to ice cream–like texture. In a small bowl, stir together the pecans and maple syrup until the nuts are evenly coated. Serve the pecans over scoops of the banana nice cream.

TIP: You could use a masticating juicer or high-speed blender to make this recipe in place of the food processor.

99. *Veggie Hummus Pinwheel s*

PREP: 10 MINUTES • COOK TIME: 0 MINUTES • TOTAL: 10 MINUTES
SERVES: 3

Ingredients:

- 3 whole-grain, spinach, flour, or gluten-free tortillas
- 3 large Swiss chard leaves
- ¾ cup Edamame Hummus or prepared hummus
- ¾ cup shredded carrots

Preparation:

Preparing the Ingredients.
Lay 1 tortilla flat on a cutting board.
Place 1 Swiss chard leaf over the tortilla.
Spread ¼ cup of hummus over the Swiss chard. Spread ¼ cup of carrots over the hummus. Starting at one end of the tortilla, roll tightly toward the opposite side.
Slice each roll-up into 6 pieces. Place in a single-serving storage container. Repeat with the remaining tortillas and filling and seal the lids.

Per Serving: Calories: 254; Fat: 8g; Protein: 10g; Carbohydrates: 39g; Fiber: 8g; Sugar: 4g; Sodium: 488mg

100. Garlic Toast

PREP: 5 MINUTES • COOK TIME: 5 MINUTES • TOTAL: 10 MINUTES SERVES: 1 SLICE

Ingredients:

- 1 teaspoon coconut oil, or olive oil
- Pinch sea salt
- 1 to 2 teaspoons nutritional yeast
- 1 small garlic clove, pressed, or ¼ teaspoon garlic powder.
- 1 slice whole-grain bread

Preparation:

Preparing the Ingredients.

In a small bowl, mix together the oil, salt, nutritional yeast, and garlic.

You can either toast the bread and then spread it with the seasoned oil or brush the oil on the bread and put it in a toaster oven to bake for 5 minutes.

If you're using fresh garlic, it's best to spread it onto the bread and then bake it.

Per Serving (1 slice): Calories: 138; Total fat: 6g; Carbs: 16g; Fiber: 4g; Protein: 7g

101. Mint Chocolate Sorbet

PREP: 5 MINUTES • COOK TIME: 0 MINUTES • TOTAL: 5 MINUTES
SERVES: 1

Ingredients:

- 1 frozen banana
- 1 tablespoon almond butter, or peanut butter, or other nut or seed butter
- 2 tablespoons fresh mint, minced.
- ¼ cup or less non-dairy milk (only if needed)
- 2 to 3 tablespoons non-dairy chocolate chips, or cocoa nibs
- 2 to 3 tablespoons goji berries (optional)

Preparation:

Preparing the Ingredients.

Put the banana, almond butter, and mint in a food processor or blender and purée until smooth.

Add the non-dairy milk if needed to keep blending (but only if needed, as this will make the texture less solid). Pulse the chocolate chips and goji berries (if using) into the mix so they're roughly chopped up.

Per Serving: Calories: 212; Total fat: 10g; Carbs: 31g; Fiber: 4g; Protein: 3g

4 WEEKS MEAL PLAN

Week 1

Day 1

Breakfast: Protein Pancake
Lunch: Buffalo chickpeas and lettuce wraps
Dinner: Sesame Tofu veggies

Day 2

Breakfast: Overnight Chia Oats
Lunch: Lentil and cheese nuggets
Dinner: Red curry mac and cheese

Day 3

Breakfast: Mexican Breakfast
Lunch: Black bean and sweet potato burritos
Dinner: Cauliflower steaks

Day 4

Breakfast: Amaranth quinoa porridge
Lunch: Mac and peas cashew sauce
Dinner: Tempeh burgers

Day 5

Breakfast: Cacao lentil Muffins
Lunch: Chickpeas, mango, and curried cauliflower salad
Dinner: Butternut squash tofu jambalaya

Day 6

Breakfast: Goji breakfast bowl
Lunch: vegetable and tofu skewers
Dinner: Vegan high protein chili

Day 7

Breakfast: Hawaiian Toast
Lunch: Baked deep-dish pancake
Dinner: Vegan chili for sore muscles

Week 2

Day 8

Breakfast: Breakfast Berry parfait
Lunch: Black bean and veggie soup
Dinner: Tofu and snow pea stir fry with peanut sauce

Day 9

Breakfast: Mini tofu Frittatas
Lunch: Spinach Pasta in pesto sauce
Dinner: Crunchy chickpea broccoli and cheese casserole

Day 10

Breakfast: Brownie pancakes
Lunch: Vegan Alfredo fettuccine pasta
Dinner: Teriyaki tofu and tempeh casserole

Day 11

Breakfast: Fig and cheese Oatmeal
Lunch: Garlic Pea Shoots
Dinner: Tomato and garlic butter beans

Day 12

Breakfast: Roasted cauliflower salad
Lunch: Tempeh vegetarian chili
Dinner: Cheesy garlicky pull apart pizza bread

Day 13

Breakfast: Mediterranean salad
Lunch: Healthy lentil soup
Dinner: Baked BBQ Tofu with caramelized onions

Day 14

Breakfast: Sweet and smoky BBQ salad
Lunch: lentil vegan soup
Dinner: Vegan Risotto with Sundried Tomatoes

Week 3

Day 15

Breakfast: Vegetarian Taco Salad
Lunch: Roasted vegetables and lentil soup
Dinner: Quinoa with peas and onion

Day 16

Breakfast: Portobello tofu fajitas
Lunch: Quinoa salad southwestern style
Dinner: Swiss chard with onions and garlic

Day 17

Breakfast: Chocolate-almond butter shake.
Lunch: Easy bean burritos
Dinner: Steamed eggplants with peanut dressing

Day 18

Breakfast: Savory tempeh sandwiches
Lunch: Sweet potato, spinach butter bean stew
Dinner: Vegan Greek meatball soup

Day 19

Breakfast: Couscous and chickpea bowls
Lunch: Tofu and mushroom soup
Dinner: Irish lamb stew

Day 20

Breakfast: Berries with Mascarpone on toasted bread
Lunch: Avocado green soup
Dinner: Cauliflower fried rice

Day 21

Breakfast: Chickpea crepes with mushrooms and spinach
Lunch: Spicy black bean soup
Dinner: Red curry mac and cheese

Week 4

Day 22

Breakfast: Vegetarian Taco Salad
Lunch: Red curry quinoa soup
Dinner: Tomato Basil Pasta

Day 23

Breakfast: Savory tempeh sandwiches
Lunch: Split pea soup
Dinner: Red curry mac and cheese

Day 24

Breakfast: Fig and cheese Oatmeal
Lunch: Lunch: Easy bean burritos
Dinner: Irish "lamb" stew

Day 25

Breakfast: Portobello tofu fajitas
Lunch: Burrito and Cauliflower Rice Bowl
Dinner: Vegan Risotto with Sundried Tomatoes

Day 26

Breakfast: Vegetarian Taco Salad
Lunch: Lentil and cheese nuggets
Dinner: Steamed eggplants with peanut dressing

Day 27

Breakfast: Savory tempeh sandwiches
Lunch: Spicy Snow Pea and Tofu Stir Fry
Dinner: Cauliflower fried rice

Day 28

Breakfast: Fig and cheese Oatmeal
Lunch: Lentil and cheese nuggets
Dinner: Red curry mac and cheese

Day 29

Breakfast: Savory tempeh sandwiches
Lunch: Tofu Sand veggies Buddha bowl
Dinner: Irish "lamb" stew

Day 30

Breakfast: Vegan sheet style pan style tofu
Lunch: Spinach Pasta in pesto sauce
Dinner: Steamed eggplants with peanut dressing

Chapter 7: Shopping list

Week 1: Shopping List

•2 packages of vegetable stock
•11 carrots
•1 package of cayenne pepper
•2 packages of cilantro
•4 lemons
•2 cans full fat coconut milk
•3 packages of coconut milk
•2 packages of psyllium husk
•1 package of raspberries
2 kiwis
•3 packages of spinach
•1 kale
•24 bananas
•1 package of spelled flour
•3 packages of ground flaxseeds
•1 package of salt
•2 packages of cinnamon
•1 package of almonds
•3 packages of hazelnuts

- 2 packages of walnuts
- 2 packages of pecans
- 1 package of dried fruit (of choice)
- 2 packages of vanilla extract
- 1 package of couscous
- 1 bottle of maple syrup
- 1 bottle of olive oil
- 3 packages of chickpeas
- 18 onions
- 1 package of cumin
- 1 package of turmeric
- 2 red peppers
- 8 sweet potatoes
- 1 package of ground coriander
- 2 packages of black beans
- 1 package of kidney beans
- 14 tomatoes
- 1 bottle of stevia
- 1 package of black pepper
- 2 packages of mushrooms
- 1 package of chili powder
- 1 package of oregano
- 1 package of thyme
- 1 package of bay leaves
- 1 can of sweet corn

- 1 bottle of lime juice
- 11 red bell peppers
- 1 peach
- 2 mangos
- 1 orange
- 1 pineapple
- 3 packages of blueberries
- 2 coconuts
- 2 packages of rolled oats
- 2 packages of coconut flour
- 2 packages of almond flour
- 1 package of red lentils
- 1 package of coconut flakes (unsweetened)
- 3 packages of hemp seeds
- 1 package of chia seeds
- 2 packages of almond milk
- 1 package of coconut oil
- 1 ginger root
- 1 package of spicy paprika powder
- 5 heads of garlic
- 1 package of tabasco sauce
- 1 bottle of MCT oil
- 1 eggplant
- 1 package of tahini
- 1 bottle of flaxseed oil

- 1 packages of baking powder
- 3 packages of coconut cream
- 1 package of cocoa powder
- 3 packages of tempeh
- 1 purple cabbage
- 2 packages of quinoa
- 1 package of soy sauce
- 1 bottle of sesame oil
- 1 bottle of rice vinegar
- 1 package of chili flakes
- 1 package of red curry paste
- 2 packages of cashews
- 2 packages of nutritional yeast
- 1 package of paprika powder
- 1 bottle of red wine
- 10 potatoes
- 2 fresh parsley
- 3 celery stalks
- 1 package of miso
- 1 papaya
- 1 yellow bell pepper
- 1 package of frozen greens (i.e. spinach, kale)
- 1 package of mixed frozen berries
- 2 sweet onions
- 1 package of whole wheat flour

•1 package of smoked paprika powder
•1 brown bread
•1 package of green chili flakes
•1 package of coconut butter
•1 package of firm tofu
•2 packages of brown rice
•1 radish
•1 cucumber
•1 package of edamame(shelled)
•1 package of sesame seeds
•1 package of cocoa butter
•1 package of vegan protein powder
•1 package of dried thyme
•1 package of broccoli
•1 package of nutmeg
•1 package of basil

Week 2: Shopping List

•3 packages of tempeh
•3 packages of quinoa
•7 red bell peppers
•1 purple cabbage
•2 sweet potatoes
•1 kale
•1 package of broccoli
•1 bottle of sesame oil
•1 bottle of soy sauce
•1 bottle of rice vinegar
•1 bottle of stevia
16 bananas
•3 packages of coconut milk
•2 packages of blueberries
•2 packages of raspberries
•2 packages of vanilla extract
•3 packages of rolled oats
•1 package of walnuts
•2 packages of chia seeds
•3 packages of black beans
•4 heads of garlic
•1 sweet onion
•3 green bell peppers
•2 packages of whole wheat flour

•2 packages of smoked paprika powder
•1 package of cumin
•1 package of salt
•1 package of pepper
•1 brown bread
•6 tortillas (whole wheat)
•2 packages of brown rice
•2 dark vegan chocolates
•1 package of vanilla-flavored vegan protein powder
•2 kiwis
•2 packages of spinach
•2 packages of ground flaxseeds
•1 pineapple
•1 mango
•1 bottle of flaxseed oil
•1 bottle of olive oil
•3 packages of hemp seeds
•2 packages of almond flour
•3 packages of baking powder
•7 red onions
•6 sweet red peppers
•2 cans (4oz) of green chilis
•1 package of dry pinto beans
•1 package of white beans

- •1 package of kidney beans
- •1 Roma tomato
- •1 package of paprika powder
- •3 fresh cilantro
- •1 avocado
- •1 package of cilantro
- •1 ginger root
- •3 green onions
- •4 zucchinis
- •1 package of sesame seeds
- •1 jar of peanut butter
- •1 package of chili flakes
- •1 bottle of maple syrup
- •1 package of almonds
- •1 package of pumpkin seeds
- •1 package of dates
- •1 vanilla stick
- •1 bottle of agave nectar
- •3 packages of almond milk
- •1 package of cinnamon
- •1 package of cayenne pepper
- •3 jalapeno peppers
- •1 yellow squash
- •1 bottle of tomato paste
- •2 cans of sweet corn

•1 package of chili powder
•1 coconut
•1 bottle of MCT oil
•3 packages of cashews
•1 lime
•1 package of oat milk
•1 package of coconut oil
•1 package of kosher salt
•1 package of whole wheat spaghetti
•1 package of tahini
•2 lemons
•1 package of Dijon mustard
•1 package of nutritional yeast
•1 package of sweet paprika powder
•1 package of nutmeg
•1 package of asparagus
•1 package of peas
•1 package of baking soda
•1 package of chickpeas
•1 package of spicy paprika powder
•1 package of baby spinach
•1 package of oregano
•1 package of avocado oil
•1 package of garlic powder
•1 bottle of canola oil

Week 3: Shopping List

- 1 bottle of olive oil
- 3 packages of black beans
- 5 green onions
- 6 red bell peppers
- 1 package of mushrooms
- 1 package of cumin
- 1 package of tabasco sauce
- 1 package of chili powder
- 1 package of salt
- 1 package of sugar
- 2 packages of whole wheat flour
- 1 package of coconut oil
- 1 package of almond butter
- 1 package of almond flour
- 4 packages of almond milk
- 1 bottle of sesame oil
- 2 packages of tofu (1 extra firm)
- 2 packages of baking soda
- 1 package of sesame seeds
- 3 zucchinis
- 1 package of rolled oats
- 1 package of oat milk
- 1 package of coconut oil

•3 packages of ground flaxseeds
•1 package of chia seeds
•1 package of vanilla sticks
•1 package of kosher salt
•1 package of cinnamon
•1 package of psyllium husk
•2 cans of full-fat coconut milk
•1 bottle of stevia
•5 lemons
•3 packages of raspberries
•1 package of almonds
•1 package of coconut flour
•2 packages of oatmeal
•13 bananas
•2 packages of hemp seeds
•1 package of lentils
•1 ginger root
•9 onions (2 yellow onions)
•1 head of garlic
•1 package of tomato paste
•1 package of curry powder
•1 package of red-hot pepper flakes
•1 jar of diced tomatoes
•1 package of pepper
•2 cilantro

•2 packages of spinach
•2 kales
•14 carrots
•6 celery stalks
•1 package of nutritional yeast
•1 package of thyme
•4 fresh parsley
•1 package of vanilla-flavored vegan protein powder
•1 dark vegan chocolate
•1 bottle of MCT oil
•1 package of cocoa powder
•1 package of brown rice
•1 package of white rice
•1 package of hazelnut
•1 package of hazelnut spread
•1 package of vanilla extract
•1 can of sweet corn
•2 packages of quinoa
•1 tomato
•6 sweet potatoes
•1 green bell pepper
•1 lime
•2 packages of blueberries
•1 package of strawberries

•1 package of blackberries
•1 bag(300g) of tortilla chips
•4 large tortillas (whole wheat)
•2 green apples
•1 package of sea salt
•1 package of red pepper flakes
•1 bottle of cherry vinegar
•1 package of black pepper
•1 package of miso
•1 package of rosemary
•2 packages of baking powder
•1 pumpkin
•1 package of dark chocolate chips (vegan friendly)
•4 jazz apples
•4 Red Delicious apples
•15 oz of tempeh
•1 purple cabbage
•1 package of broccoli
•1 package of soy sauce
•1 bottle of rice vinegar
•2 packages of cashews
•1 package of chili flakes
•1 package of red curry paste
•2 packages of coconut milk

- 2 packages of coconut cream
- 1 kiwi
- 2 apples
- 1 pineapple
- 1 mango
- 1 package of couscous
- 1 package of chickpeas
- 1 red pepper
- 1 package of cayenne pepper
- 1 package of cilantro
- 1 package of coriander
- 1 package of ground turmeric
- 2 packages of vegetable stock
- 1 bottle of avocado oil
- 1 package of garlic powder
- 1 package of oregano
- 3 Chioggia beets
- 2 avocados
- 1 package of wasabi powder
- 1 package of sushi rice
- 2 packages of edamame beans
- 1 package of pecans
- 1 package of matcha powder
- 1 package of freeze-dried peach powder
- 1 eggplant

•1 package of tahini
•1 package of coconut butter
•1 package of sriracha
•1 package of brown sugar
•1 package of wasabi paste
•1 package of pickled ginger

Week 4: Shopping List

•2 packages of brown rice
•1 bottle of olive oil
•2 packages of portobello mushrooms
•3 packages of cashews
•1 package of basil leaves
•1 bottle of red wine
•1 package of nutritional yeast
•1 package of pepper
•11 onions (3 red, 2 white, 1 green, 2 brown)
•2 heads of garlic
•4 carrots
•7 celery stalks
•8 sweet potatoes
•2 kales
•9 bell peppers (1 green, red and yellow)

•1 package of thyme
•1 package of miso
•4 fresh parsley
•1 fresh cilantro
•1 package of rosemary
•1 package of miso
•1 package of peanut butter
•1 package of cocoa powder
•3 packages of coconut flour
•1 package of vanilla-flavored vegan protein powder
•1 package of cumin
•1 package of cayenne pepper
•1 package of tahini
•3 packages of baking powder
•3 packages of chickpeas
•4 green apples
13 bananas
•2 oranges
•1 ginger root
•3 lemons
•2 kiwis
•3 packages of coconut milk
•2 packages of walnuts
•1 package of goji berries

- 1 package of pumpkin seeds
- 2 packages of rolled oats
- 3 packages of almonds
- 1 package of hemp seeds
- 1 package of salt
- 1 bottle of agave nectar
- 1 package of dates
- 2 packages of vanilla extract
- 1 bottle of MCT oil
- 1 bottle of stevia
- 1 package of spinach
- 1 ginger root
- 1 cucumber
- 3 packages of blueberries
- 2 packages of raspberries
- 1 package of coconut butter
- 2 packages of almond flour
- 1 package of almonds
- 1 package of full-fat coconut milk
- 1 package of freeze-dried blueberry powder
- 2 packages of black beans
- 1 package of white beans
- 2 jalapenos
- 4 large tomatoes
- 1 dark vegan chocolate

•1 package of hazelnuts
•2 packages of coconut cream
•1 bottle of agave nectar
•1 package of chia seeds
•1 package of glucomannan powder
•1 bottle of flaxseed oil
•1 pumpkin
•1 package of onion powder
•1 package of bay leaves
•1 package of almond butter
•2 packages of baking soda
•1 package of paprika powder
•1 package of coconut oil
•1 package of tabasco sauce
•1 eggplant
•1 pineapple
•1 mango
•1 coconut
•2 cans (14 oz) unsweetened coconut milk
•1 cans dice green chilies
•1 package of curry powder
•15 oz tempeh
•1 purple cabbage
•2 packages of quinoa
•1 package of soy sauce

•1 package of broccoli
•1 bottle of sesame oil
•1 bottle of rice vinegar
•1 package of red curry paste
•1 package of garlic powder
•1 package of strawberries
•1 package of black berries
•1 zucchini
•1 bottle of white wine vinegar
•1 package of vegan BBQ sauce
•1 lime
•1 package of cinnamon
•1 package of whole wheat flour
•1 package of sesame seeds

Conclusion

Following the vegan diet has become extremely popular over the past decade.

People switch for ethical and health reasons, and it is a great diet for people who are serious about getting healthy.

But the one group of people that are still strongly judged about begin vegans are bodybuilders.

It has been a belief that the only way a person can gain muscle is by eating a bunch of lean poultry, dairy, and eggs. But the fact of the matter is, you can eat vegan and still gain muscle, and that is what this book is going to show you. Vegans come from all walks of life. They are of every nationality and every race. Being a vegan is more of a philosophy and lifestyle choice than it is an actual diet. The reasons for becoming a vegan could be to obtain better health, for environmental reasons, or due to the ethical concerns surrounding animal rights. Whatever the reasons may be for you, there is overwhelming evidence that shows how much healthier a vegan diet is for everyone, not just aspiring athletes. Some of the world's best athletes are vegan. This would not have been possible if a vegan diet had not met the needs of their bodies and increased their performance.

While many believe that a completely vegan diet is a new concept, it literally goes back almost until the dawn of human time. Everyone is familiar with the Roman Gladiators. These athletes fought wild boars, lions, and each other in arenas cheered on by thousands of people. Discoveries in recent years have shown that the diet for most Gladiators was vegan. Even back then they were able to see the benefits that a vegan diet had on their performance while training and while fighting inside the arena.

A vegan diet has many health benefits. But is a vegan diet beneficial to an athlete?

Research has shown that diets that are high in foods from natural and unrefined sources play a great part in improving general health, immune systems, and cardio health.

Lightning Source UK Ltd.
Milton Keynes UK
UKHW021552240221
379245UK00004B/63

9 781914 15441